THE TEXAS RANGERS

THE
TEXAS
RANGERS

★

by **WILL HENRY**

Illustrated by **CHARLES BANKS WILSON**

RANDOM HOUSE · NEW YORK

Contents

Foreword vii

PART ONE

1 The Four Horsemen of the Far West 3
2 The War Clouds Gather 8
3 First Blood for Private Smithwick 14
4 Lieutenant Rice and the Cherokee Uprising 22
5 The Day the Rangers Stayed Away 31
6 Colonel Karnes and the Council House Fight 37
7 Comanche Vengeance 45
8 Plum Creek and Ben McCulloch's Ride 51

PART TWO

9 John C. Hays, Savior of San Antonio 65
10 Captain Jack Sets a Trap at Salado 70
11 Bigfoot Wallace and the Black Bean 76
12 The Rangers "Win" the Mexican War 83
13 Rip Ford and the Ten-Year Wait 90
14 The Private War of Cheno Cortinas 100
15 McNelly and His Men 109

PART THREE

16 The Hunting of John Wesley Hardin 121
17 Major Jones and the Frontier Battalion 132

18   The Kimble County "Round-up"   137
19   Sam Bass, the Ballad-Writers' Bandit   143
20   The Last of the Great Bad Men   154
21   End of the Ranger Trail   164

Epilogue   The Texas Ranger Today   173

Bibliography   175

Index   177

This is the true story of the most feared and famous organization of frontier fighters for law and order in American history. The events depicted herein are taken from actual Ranger records. Some minor details and descriptions have had to be supplied by the author, since many of the official records of the force prior to the Civil War were destroyed by fires. The essential facts are faithful to the heroic memories of the gallant officers and men of The Texas Rangers who created them.

W. H.

PART I

PART 1

The Comanches

Oh, pray for the ranger
You kind-hearted stranger,
He has roamed o'er the prairies
For many a year;
He has kept the Comanches
From off your ranches,
And chased them far over
The Texas frontier. . . .

OLD TEXAS BALLAD

1

The Four Horsemen
of the Far West

To understand the grim and violent nature of the Ranger's work, one must first understand the grim and violent nature of the enemy against whom he fought.

And to do that, one must be able to command his imagination to march back across more than one hundred years of history to the time when Texas was young. There was no law whatever then in all her quarter-million square miles of raw wilderness—*until the Rangers came.*

The Rangers were always outnumbered by the enemy. The odds were frequently four to one, five to one, and even ten to one. Yet time and again these fearless men answered their captain's cheery call of "Follow me, men!" straight into the face of certain death.

And, somehow, time and again, when the last bark of Colt or Winchester had growled off across the silent prairie, it was not the Texas Rangers who were bewailing the loss of comrades dear or bemoaning the departure of brave brothers suddenly called away. *It was the enemy.*

Who was this enemy?

He was of three types.

First, he was the High Plains Horseback Indian, raiding and burning deep into the peaceful settlements. He murdered the luckless white man wherever he might find him—by his lonely campfire, standing guard over his livestock, or in the peaceful slumber of his cabin bed.

Second, the enemy was the crafty Mexican Border Bandit, the vengeful vaquero of Old Mexico. Striking in the dead of night across the Rio Grande, he seized and drove off the horses and cattle herds upon which his American neighbor depended for his very life.

Third, he was the brutal American Bad Man—the cold-eyed gunman, the killer, who flooded into Texas following the Civil War. The Bad Man preyed mercilessly upon friend and foe alike and knew no law but that of the deadly Colt Revolver.

These, then, were the enemies of Texas. And this was the order in which they appeared to rob and slay the brave pioneers of the new land.

To fight them—to hunt them down and kill them like the outlaw animals they were—became the dangerous job of the Texas Ranger.

The Ranger was thus, in the very beginning, a product of grim circumstances and violent times.

He never killed a man he did not have to kill, but he had to kill many men.

He swore, in the oath he took, never to surrender himself, nor his arms; never to desert a comrade, never to retreat. Yet he was commanded, always, to give the enemy the first shot!

He brought the only law to a vast and desolate land —a land so big that one famous captain actually rode a far-flung, circling patrol of 1,600 miles in 30 days without once coming near its borders!

The Ranger had no regular uniform. No badge, no battle flag, no insignia of rank. No company doctor, no medical care, no military benefits whatever. He had to furnish his own arms and his own horse—a good one, at that, worth at least $100! With his meager pay, he had to provide all expenses of both his mount and himself. For the magnificent reward of $37.50 a month (which as often as not was never paid) he was privileged to risk his life in the name of frontier law and order.

The great wonder remains that he would accept such terrible odds of Indian, bandit and bad man for this miserable pay.

The proud answer to that is that the Ranger never fought for money. He fought for a land—Texas. And he fought for a cause—freedom from fear and oppression.

And as he fought, so he was—a man made up of equal parts of the three dangerous forces which had created him.

He could trail with the savage cunning of a Comanche brave.

He could ride with the furious skill of the Mexican vaquero.

He could shoot with the quiet-eyed deadliness of a Tennessee mountaineer.

He was the finest individual fighting man the West ever produced. He faced the greatest odds, with the least possible chance of success, of any law officer in frontier history.

This is his true story.

Turn back the clock of time a century and more!

Spring to saddle and ride with the Texas wind

through blind-black river thickets, over blazing sunlit prairies, across burning desert and snow-swept mountain passes.

Take the dark and desperate trail of the Four Horsemen of the Far West: the Comanche brave, the Mexican bandit, the American bad man and the Texas Ranger.

Follow it with the latter, the deadliest rider of them all.

Share, with him, his lonely outpost camp. Eat with him beside his cheery mesquite fire. Sleep with him beneath the wheeling southwest stars. Fight with him inside the screaming circle of the Indian ambush. Laugh with him against the hopeless odds of the closing Mexican cavalry trap. Stand beside him as he meets the thunder of American outlaw guns.

Come meet his famous captains and his fearless men.

Peer back into their wondrous times through the gunsmoke of a hundred years.

Ride again with the Texas Rangers!

2

The War Clouds Gather

The Americans first came into the Spanish province of Texas with Moses Austin in 1820. They settled the rich and beautiful bottom lands between the Colorado and the Trinity rivers.

The following year, Mexico revolted against Spain. As a result, Texas became a member province of the new Republic of Mexico.

Shortly thereafter, the leadership of the American colony passed to its founder's talented son, Stephen Austin.

Young Austin wisely made his peace with Mexico. But for several years the little colony hovered between success and failure.

To aid it in its brave struggle, Mexico passed a generous law encouraging more Americans to settle in Texas.

Hungry and greedy people in the United States took sudden notice of the rich new lands to be had for nothing. They came in a wave. By 1830, this flood of American fortune hunters had gotten out of hand. The Mexican Government could no longer control them. They would not pay taxes nor obey the laws.

So Mexico abruptly closed the borders of Texas to further emigration from the United States.

But the action came too late.

In 1835, the belligerent Texans revolted. For a full year they fought like savages against the Mexican Army. Finally, the Mexican dictator General Santa Anna was defeated disastrously on the field of San Jacinto. Texas had won her independence. She was now a sovereign nation, responsible to no one but herself.

The saga of her famous Rangers followed swiftly.

The actual ordinance which created the first official corps of Texas Rangers provided for three companies of 56 men each.

Each company was officered by a captain and a first and second lieutenant.

A major commanded the entire corps, subject to the orders of the commander in chief of the army. The latter, of course, was fiery old Sam Houston, first president of the Republic of Texas.

Privates were enlisted for one year. They were paid $1.25 a day for all expenses of themselves and their horses. Officers were paid the same as officers of equal rank in the United States service forces.

Each Ranger was ordered always to be ready with "a good horse, saddle, bridle and blanket, and a hundred rounds of powder and ball."

Then came the disturbing part of the ordinance.

The Rangers were named a "special body of irregular troops." As such, they were entirely set apart from the regular army of Texas, as well as from her volunteer militia.

This seemed like an innocent distinction at first. But it was not. It went deep into the heart of an uneasy frontier tradition and distrust of vigilante forces.

The Texans were suddenly very worried.

Many good citizens of the young nation shook their heads uncertainly at this delegation of "special powers" to an irregular force.

"We have created a ragtag monster!" warned one of the founding fathers. "This rough band of cutthroat horsemen may very well decide to make their own laws as they ride along!"

Rangers were a "special body of irregular troops"

This was no idle nightmare. The thoughtful citizens realized that at once.

Frontier history was full of dark chapters written by such night-riding bands of hard-eyed volunteers. "Stranglers" they were called, after their vicious habit of first hanging their captives to the nearest gallows tree, and only then inquiring into their real guilt or innocence.

So the grim warning struck its chill into many a heart and mind throughout the settlements.

Where vigilante groups had done as much before, what was to keep the Texas Rangers from turning into a lawless band of midnight stranglers? What was to hinder them from becoming as much of a menace to peaceful citizens as to the savage enemy?

The unhappy settlers did not know.

They could only hope.

Actually, the "Special Force" had been created for one reason alone. That was to defend the isolated western frontier against Indian raids while Texas was fighting her war of independence with Mexico.

But the Rangers had had little chance to prove themselves. The Indians had been wisely quiet during the war.

And why not? argued the crafty warriors. Why bother killing the hated *Tejanos* (Texans) when their

Mexican brothers were doing such a good job of it for them?

So the fierce braves had stayed home.

As a result, the frustrated Rangers had been made to look worse than useless.

With little or nothing to do, they had taken to quarreling among themselves and to making considerable trouble in the various frontier settlements where they were quartered.

But what would happen now?

The war was over and the Indians were raiding again with all their oldtime, savage fury.

Would the Rangers do anything now?

That was the somber question over which the worried settlement fathers exchanged uncertain looks. And for the answer to it they turned their anxious glances westward toward Comancheland.

The Rangers did not keep them waiting.

3

First Blood for Private Smithwick

It was early January, 1836. The night was freezing cold in the Ranger camp at Hornsby's station, ten miles below Austin on the Colorado River. A sleety rain was driving in from the north, chilling the thinly clad riders, hunching the nervous rumps of their mounts on the picket line. The cookfires went out repeatedly. The water for the coffee could not be brought to boil. The howl of the wind rose higher.

The men gathered here belonged to Captain Tumlinson's company. This was one of the three original companies of Texas Rangers created only a few months before.

The men were new to one another and to their commander. They had been on the Indian frontier seven weeks, yet none of them had seen a redskin nor heard a war whoop. Their nerves were worn thin with the waiting. Their strength was sapped by the constant day-and-night riding after an enemy who had seemingly disappeared. And yet, wherever the Rangers were not to be seen, there the red men would spring up to kill and burn. Then they would disappear again before their pursuers could catch them.

In the settlements ugly talk sprang up. The Rangers were a quarrelsome, trouble-making lot, some said. Others claimed that the Rangers made no real effort to find and punish the Indians; they only sat in camp, drew their pay and looked the other way when a ranch was burned or a lonely settler was scalped in his corn-field. Disband them, urged these critics. The Rangers were a bad lot. The sooner they were done away with, the better it would be for the Texas taxpayer.

So went the talk.

Meanwhile, Private Noah Smithwick of Tumlinson's company was nodding over the miserable smoke of his sentry fire. Beyond him, his few companions were struggling with the balky flames of their supper fires, trying to achieve a sodden meal of moldy bacon and rain-soaked corn bread. Suddenly Ranger Smithwick's weary eyes were staring at a ghostly apparition staggering toward him from the dripping blackness of the river timber.

No words could ever improve upon Smithwick's own account of what followed.

"Suddenly," the startled young Ranger tells us, "a white woman, an entire stranger, her clothes hanging in shreds about her torn and bleeding body, dragged herself into camp and sank exhausted to the ground.

"When at length she recovered, she told us that her name was Hibbons. That, in company with her husband, brother and two small children, she was journeying overland up to their little home on the Guadalupe, when they were attacked by a band of Comanches. The two men were killed, the wagon plundered, herself and the children made prisoners. She was bound onto one of the mules and her little three-year-old boy on the other.

"The second child was a young babe. The poor little creature, whose sufferings the mother could not allay, cried continuously. At once, one of the redskins snatched it from her and dashed its brains out against a tree.

"The cunning redskins knew there was little risk of their outrage being discovered quickly. When a cold rainy norther met them at the crossing of the Colorado they sought the shelter of a cedar brake and lay by to wait for it to subside. Wrapping themselves in their buffalo robes, they were soon sound asleep.

"But there was no sleep for Mrs. Hibbons.

"The brave woman knew that there was no time to lose. Another day's travel would take her so far beyond the reach of the settlements that it would be impossible for her to escape and procure help before the savages reached their stronghold.

"She waited only until assured by their breathing that her captors were asleep. Then, summoning all her courage, she carefully tucked a robe about her sleeping child and stole away, forced to leave him to the mercies of the brutal barbarians.

"She felt sure the river they had crossed was the Colorado. She knew there were settlements below. She made straight for the river, hiding her tracks in its icy waters. Fearful of pursuit and discovery by the Indians, she had spent nearly twenty-four hours traveling the distance of but ten miles to Hornsby's station.

"Fortunate, beyond hope, in finding the Rangers there, she implored us to save her child. She described the mule he rode, the band of Indians and the direction they were traveling.

"Hastily dispatching our supper," Ranger Smithwick reports, "we were soon in the saddle."

The newly commissioned Rangers were indeed soon

in the saddle. Retribution followed with deadly swiftness for the murderous red men. Private Smithwick again takes up the tale:

"With our trusty guide, Reuben Hornsby, we traveled on until we judged that we must be near the trail. Fearful of crossing it in the darkness, we halted and waited for daylight.

"As soon as it was light enough, our scouts were out and soon found the trail. It was fresh and well defined. The marauders did not seem to be at all alarmed as to the consequences of their prisoner's escape. It was about 10 o'clock in the morning when we came upon them just preparing to break camp.

"Taken completely by surprise they broke for the shelter of a cedar brake leaving everything save their weapons. I was riding a fleet horse which, becoming excited, carried me right in among the fleeing savages. One of them jumped behind a tree and fired on me with his musket.

"Unable to control my horse, I jumped off him and gave chase to my assailant on foot, knowing his gun was empty. I fired on him and had the satisfaction of seeing him fall. Leaving him for dead, I ran on, hoping to bring down another.

"But the brave I had shot lay flat on the ground and loaded his gun. He discharged it at Captain Tumlinson, narrowly missing him and killing his horse.

The shot narrowly missed Captain Tumlinson

Ranger Conrad Rohrer ran up and, snatching the gun from the Indian's hand, dealt him a blow on the head, crushing his skull.

"We then achieved the main object of the expedition which was the rescue of the little Hibbons boy. The Indians, careful of the preservation of their small captive—they intended to make a good Comanche of him—had wrapped him warmly in their finest buffalo robe. When we rushed upon them, they had no chance to remove him.

"The other Indians," concludes Private Smithwick, with that rare sense of understatement which was to become the trademark of the Rangers, "made good their escape into the cedar brake.

"The scene of the rescue," he adds softly, "was on Walnut Creek, about ten miles northwest of Austin. There was a suspicious moisture in many an eye long since a stranger to tears, when the overjoyed mother clasped her only remaining treasure to her heart. . . ."

The aftermath of Captain Tumlinson's bold night ride after the Comanche killers brought more than a few manly tears to a lonely handful of tough young Rangers on the Indian frontier. It brought to the Texas settlers the happy realization that the Texas Rangers, for all their poor pay and threadbare garb, meant deadly business.

Overnight, the feeling changed. The frightened pioneers had found a champion at last.

From this time forward, any Indian who came into the settlements to burn and kill would do so only with the certain knowledge that within the day, perhaps the hour of his evil deed, the Texas Rangers would be riding his bloody trail.

It was indeed but a small beginning in the Rangers' promised war against the fierce Comanche—only one Indian killed and one white child recovered. Yet it *was* a beginning. And it stopped the settlement talk of disbanding the force. The "rough band of cutthroat horsemen" had proved itself. No one in Texas could know when or where the Indian fire would next burst into flames. But everyone now knew that whenever or wherever it did, the "ragtag" Rangers would be there to put it out.

4

Lieutenant Rice and the Cherokee Uprising

It was May 18, 1839. Lieutenant Jim Rice was worried, and for a very good reason. Things were entirely too quiet that late spring morning along the San Gabriel Fork of the Little River. And he did not like at all the Indian sign he was staring at in the damp sand of the riverbank.

He halted his small patrol of Captain Andrews' company of Texas Rangers on the east shore of the lonely stream. Low-voiced, he consulted his lean, gray-eyed sergeant, Innes Simms.

There was disturbing cause for hesitation.

For three years now the Rangers had roamed the frontier in ceaseless pursuit and punishment of the raiding red men. The battle had been fierce and constant. There had been no respite for the handful of hard-riding volunteers who had sworn never to surrender to the enemy. All during those three restless years the Indians had struck almost daily against the white settlements.

Now—suddenly—for the past three weeks, not a single painted warrior had been seen.

It was as though the silent prairie had opened wide and swallowed up the wild red horsemen.

Why?

What were the wily savages up to?

It was a big part of Lieutenant Jim Rice's job to find the answer to that grim question.

He had one dark clue.

For months Texas had been hearing rumors of a sinister plot. The Mexicans, eager to retrieve the loss of Texas to the hated *Tejanos,* were at work on a devilish scheme to win it back. The plan was chillingly simple —to incite all the Indian tribes in Texas and stir them into uniting with the Mexicans and rising up to massacre every white *Tejano* between Red River on the north and the Rio Grande on the south.

The rumor further hinted that the revolt of the red

men was to start with the most powerful tribe in the east—the Cherokees. Then it was to spread with the speed of prairie fire to the Indian warlords of the west —the Comanches.

Yet, the closest watch and most diligent patrols of the Army and militia had failed to reveal a single positive proof of the existence of such a plot on the part of the Indians and Mexicans.

In fact, there was every evidence to the contrary. The Comanches were still raiding. As long as they continued to do so, the Texans could know they were not uniting with anybody. They were still doing their bloody business in the same old way—every roving band for itself.

That was the situation up to three weeks ago.

Now it was ominously different.

In the three weeks since young Lieutenant Jim Rice had reached the frontier there had been no Indian raids whatever. His orders had been to lead his Rangers in pursuit of the rumor the Army and militia had been unable to track down. He and his little company were to do everything in their power to seek out some proof of the threatened uprising. Yet in the whole three weeks they had not seen a single redskin pony track, *until this hushed moment.*

There was not the slightest doubt about what the Lieutenant was staring at now.

The sign which had halted his tiny command on the banks of the San Gabriel was a deep-pressed trail of unshod Indian war-pony hoof prints. They were only hours old. And they angled straight across the silent stream toward Mexico.

Nor was that all.

In the lead of the unshod hoof marks lay a single line of alien pony tracks—a set of sharp-cut prints such as were left only by the iron-shod feet of a white man's mount. *Or a Mexican's.*

"What do you think, Innes?" said the youthful officer at last in a husky voice.

"Same as you, Jim," grunted his weather-beaten sergeant. "That there shod horse ain't got no good business in among them barefoot Injun ponies."

"Could be a Mexican. Is that it?"

"That's it," said Sergeant Innes Simms.

"Only one way to find out for sure, I reckon," murmured Lieutenant Jim Rice.

"I reckon," said the grizzled sergeant, nodding in agreement.

Jim Rice turned to his waiting Rangers.

"Follow me, men," he said quietly. And he spurred his bright bay gelding across the shallow stream toward Old Mexico.

The Rangers rode hard. The trail was broad and easy

to read. It told of a big band, perhaps as many as thirty braves, with more than a hundred stolen horses. Lieutenant Rice had seventeen men, including himself and a friendly Lipan Apache tracker.

He did not hesitate.

Two-to-one were far better odds than the Texas Rangers were accustomed to getting. They rode on.

At six o'clock in the evening, the Lipan tracker halted his pony. He held up a warning hand, motioning the young officer forward. The Indians were just ahead, in the heavy timber along the small stream beyond the next rise.

"Follow me, men," Lieutenant Rice told his Rangers

Lieutenant Rice hesitated now.

That "small stream" was the San Gabriel, the same body of water the Rangers had left that morning. In twelve hours of trailing, the Indians had swung completely about and come back to it. Did that mean they knew they were being followed? Would they be waiting in ambush for the outnumbered Rangers?

Lieutenant Rice did not know. Nor could he wait to find out.

The sun was already low. The prairie twilight would follow swiftly. In the succeeding darkness the treacherous red horsemen could easily slip away to safety across the Mexican border.

"Follow me, men," said the white-faced youth for the second time that day.

"You heard the Lieutenant, boys!" Sergeant Innes Simms grinned. "Let's go!"

And go the Rangers did. Up and over the river rise and swooping down upon the startled Indians beyond it.

The red men were just putting their ponies out to graze, after having watered them in the stream. They had no chance to mount them. They ran for the trees at the riverbank, firing back at the charging Rangers.

Three of the Indians were shot down in the first rush. The others succeeded in reaching the river timber. From this shelter, they fired back so desperately that the Rangers were forced to fall back. They took what cover they could and continued to pour a hot fire into the tangled brush which hid the Indians.

Darkness ended the attack. Under its cover, the remaining red men stole away. They left the huge herd of Texas horses and the bodies of their three dead comrades.

Young Lieutenant Rice advanced to claim the spoils of his first Indian fight.

What he found there in the lonely darkness made his brief encounter with the enemy one of the most important Indian battles in Texas history.

For only two of the dead men were Indians.

The third was a Mexican.

And upon the bullet-riddled body of Manuel Flores, the dead Mexican, Lieutenant Jim Rice found the evidence he was seeking.

It was all there in the blood-stained document which Jim Rice took from a secret pocket in the Mexican leader's jacket.

According to that document, the Indians were to gather north of San Antonio as soon as the new grass came in 1839. A Mexican force of 5,000 cavalry and infantry was to cross the border and join up with them west of the white men's settlements. All Texans were to be killed or driven out of the country. The land was to be returned to the Indians and to be divided equally among the tribes taking part in the uprising. Meanwhile, the Indians were to cease all raids on the settlements, lulling the Texans into a sense of security. The ordinarily peaceful Cherokees of east Texas were named as the principal tribe involved in Act One of the Great Massacre.

That was enough for Lieutenant Rice. He did not linger on the banks of the San Gabriel. For this was 1839. The new grass was already well up. The Indian raids had ceased three weeks earlier.

Did that mean the eastern tribes were already gathered? Did it mean that the Mexican invasion force was even now poised and waiting to strike across the border?

Again, Lieutenant Rice could not know. And again he could not wait to find out.

Within the hour his weary men were riding once more, pressing homeward with the mysterious document which could mean the difference between life and death for the young Republic of Texas.

As he spurred his bay gelding onward through the night, Lieutenant Rice was sure of but one thing. Thinking of it, his heart swelled with pride, his tired body straightened in the saddle. In that long gone moment of prairie darkness, twenty-five miles from the capital city of Austin, Lieutenant James O. Rice sat very tall on his little bay pony.

He had the fate of Texas sealed safely in his breast pocket. *And the Texas Rangers had put it there!*

5

The Day the Rangers Stayed Away

The proud annals of the Texas Rangers are as full of things they did *not* do as of things they did.

Having uncovered the Mexican-Indian plot in time to render it harmless, they had done their dangerous duty in full. They took no official part in the brutal expulsion of the Cherokees from Texas which followed. But since that expulsion set the stage for their first great era—their no-quarter war with the western Comanches—it must be briefly considered.

When the Manuel Flores papers captured by Rice's

Rangers were made public, the panicky citizens demanded action. They got it.

Old Sam Houston, that tall and towering friend of the red man, was no longer in office. The new president, Mirabeau Buonaparte Lamar, hated all Indians with deep passion. Under his orders, the army of Texas was at once dispatched to drive the Cherokees from their highly cultivated lands in the eastern settlements. This, despite the fact that there was no proof at all that their chiefs had agreed to the treacherous proposals of the Mexican war agents.

The fact that the Cherokees had made no preparation to take part in the vicious plot did not save them. They were Indians. They were taking up some of the best farmland in Texas. They had to go or be driven out.

A party of four "peace commissioners" was sent to parley with the head chief, Bowles. Their real purpose was to make sure the Cherokees did not leave before the Army troops got into position to "help them go."

The brave Bowles, though he knew his cause was already lost, could not bow down to the bandit demands of the greedy Texans. Though they wore no masks, they were simply robbing him and his people, and the old chief knew it. But he was unafraid. His people, he announced with pathetic dignity, would fight.

It was what the Texans had wanted to hear. And it was all they wanted to hear.

The hopeless encounter lasted less than forty-eight hours. It was brought to its shameful close when Chief Bowles was captured and shot down in cold blood.

Leaderless, stunned by this turn of events after twenty years of faithful friendship to the white man in Texas, the sorrowful survivors of the most civilized Indian tribe in American history fled northward into the wilderness of Arkansas.

But even this wasn't enough for the Texans. Caught up in the fever of their long-standing fear of the red warriors, the white troops decided to make a clean sweep of it. They fell upon the remaining East Texas tribes and drove them after the Cherokees. To this outbreak of "pure piracy upon the plains" the Delawares, Shawnees, Caddos, Kickapoos, Creeks and Seminoles were shocked and unbelieving victims.

Yet they had no chance. They knew that. They were being punished for the scalpings and cabin-burnings of their ancestors. Against such a charge there was no safety but to follow the panic-stricken example of the Cherokees.

From the loblolly pine forests of the Sabine to the inner prairies of the Brazos, the Indians of eastern Texas gathered up their loved ones and fled for their lives.

Within short weeks a great silence fell over the settlements. For the first time in nineteen years the throb of the dance drum and the shrill of the war whoop were heard no more. The cookfires no longer smoked. The council houses stood deserted. Only the restless wind prowled the village streets. The Indian was gone.

The last pitiful remnant of his former power—a small band of Cherokees lost from the main band and trying to reach the safety of Mexico—were surrounded and destroyed on the west bank of the Colorado.

Among the dead was John Bowles, beloved son of the old chief.

The so-called Cherokee Uprising was over. The despised redskin had been driven forever from the settled eastern part of Texas.

The good citizens of the new Republic looked on and nodded "well done" at the sinful work.

But they nodded too soon.

For the Great Spirit had not forgotten his red children.

Out on the trackless western plains, Lone Wolf listened in slant-eyed silence to the news of the Cherokee disaster.

Lone Wolf was the war chief of all the Comanches. He was a wise and crafty leader. He knew the white man well. When he heard what had befallen Bowles and his gentle people, he knew he must act fast.

"Paint your faces," Lone Wolf ordered his tribesmen

Within the hour, he had gathered his dark-skinned sub-chiefs into high council.

He had one frightening question for them.

If the pale-faced *Tejanos* could do this monstrous thing to Indians who were their faithful friends, what might they do to red men who were their bitter enemies?

Lone Wolf did not know the answer to his own question. But one thing was certain. He had to find that answer, and find it fast!

The old chief stood up. He put away his pipe and reached for his war shield. The council was at an end.

"Paint your faces and tell your women good-bye," he told his scowling listeners. "Take your best ponies and make your strongest medicine. We are going to the white man's big village where the Mexican Black Robes used to live.

"We are going to San Antonio——!"

6

Colonel Karnes and the
Council House Fight

The new year of 1840 was nine days old. The January
sun was warm and bright in the Plaza of old San
Antonio. The two guards on duty in front of the Bexar
County Rangers headquarters were in understandably
excellent humor.

"I allow," drawled Private Pettus Tucker, "that
you and me had best be lookin' for a new job, Bates.
I ain't seen a Comanche for so long I forgot what one
looks like."

Corporal Bates Isbell, on the point of agreeing with

his friend, took another look down the dusty street. His eyes narrowed suddenly. "Take a good squint yonder," he said softly. "Mebbe it'll freshen your memory!"

Ranger Tucker peered hard. His good-natured grin faded. Riding slowly across the Plaza, the sparkling winter sun flashing off their tasseled lances and gaudily painted buffalo-hide shields, were three Comanche war chiefs.

"Reckon I'd better run in and tell the Colonel," muttered Private Pettus Tucker.

"Reckon you better had," agreed Corporal Bates Isbell, easing his big horse pistol in its worn holster.

Inside the headquarters building Colonel Henry W. Karnes, San Antonio's famous red-haired Indian fighter, put down his turkey-feather pen. He laid aside the peaceful report he had been writing to General Albert Sidney Johnson, Texas Secretary of War. He reached, instead, for his long Sharps rifle.

"All right, Tucker," he said quickly. "Bring them in. Let's see what the red scoundrels want this time. I'll bet they've had enough of the Texas Rangers and want to quit."

Colonel Karnes was right. Lone Wolf's first words told him that.

"My people are tired of war," the old chief began nervously.

Lone Wolf did not like standing inside the little houses of the white men. The thick walls and the narrow rifle-slit windows made him feel as though he were standing in a trap. He got on quickly with what he had come to say.

"We are ready to put aside our shields and lay down our lances. We want to ask the Rangers for peace."

Colonel Karnes looked at him. A grim smile of deep pride and satisfaction lit his lean face.

The Comanches wanted to ask *the Rangers* for peace!

After four years of fierce warfare against the *whole army* of the new Republic, the wild men of the plains had come in to beg for peace from a tiny company of *twenty-five* Texas Rangers!

No wonder Colonel Karnes felt proud.

But his smile was gone as swiftly as it had appeared.

No peace treaty was possible, he told the three chiefs. Not until the Comanches agreed to bring in all the white captives in their possession.

Lone Wolf and his companions muttered angrily among themselves. Colonel Karnes warned them they had but five minutes to make up their minds. Their ugly scowls grew darker.

Colonel Karnes took out his gold watch. He propped it on his desk, against the heavy barrel of his rifle. The Indians took the silent hint.

It was agreed, they nodded sullenly. They would return in twenty days with all the prisoners.

Colonel Karnes went back to his report. His quill pen scratched across the rough paper with urgent speed.

He had no faith in the Comanche promise, he wrote General Johnson. And his Rangers would not take part in any further talks with them. The treacherous red men had lied too many times. The government had better send a strong body of regular troops to San Antonio at once. The Rangers' job was done. They had fought the savage foe for four bloody years. Now he was beaten and wanted to surrender. The war was over. Making peace was for politicians. Colonel Henry W. Karnes respectfully excused himself.

He and his Texas Rangers wanted no part in the foolish business of "trying to bring sweetness and light to the murdering Comanche."

Two months later, on March 19th, a trio of dark-skinned runners appeared suddenly from the west. When the citizens of San Antonio heard their news they began putting up their heavy wooden shutters. The Indians were coming! Like the Rangers, the frontier townsfolk had no use for any kind of an Indian but a "good" one. In Ranger language, this meant one with a Texan bullet hole between his eyes.

Lieutenant Colonel William S. Fisher, in command

of the Army troops stationed around the Council House, had no such prejudices. He prepared to receive the Indian delegation in good faith.

But when its sullen chiefs stood before him, the officer perceived at once that he had been tricked.

There were plenty of Comanches present, *but only one white captive.*

Fisher knew that no less than half a hundred white women and children had been seized and carried off by the red barbarians during the preceding four years.

"What is the meaning of this!" he demanded angrily. "Where are all the prisoners you promised to bring in to this talk?"

Lone Wolf was not present. Like Colonel Karnes, he was not a man of peace. Instead, he had sent his crafty medicine man, Muk-war-rah.

Muk-war-rah was an evil-looking man. He was shaved completely bald. His skull-like face and copper chest were smeared with ochre and vermilion war paint.

"We have brought in the only one we had," he said, grinning wolfishly. "The others are with other tribes." Then, striking his breast and leering full into the white officer's face, he challenged insolently, "How do you like the answer?"

Lieutenant Colonel Fisher did not like the answer at all. The Rangers had been right, as usual. There

The Comanches brought in only one white captive

was no reasonable hope whatever of making a treaty with these arrogant killers. They understood only one kind of talk—the harsh language that a loaded rifle and a naked cavalry saber spoke.

"Bar the door!" Fisher snapped to the soldiers outside. Then, "You are prisoners," he told Muk-war-rah and the warriors inside the room with him. "We will hold you until every one of the captives is brought in!"

Fisher knew that the Indians knew what he was talking about. The lone captive, a little girl named

Matilda Lockhart, had told him that there were many other white children and several women still in the Comanche camp. The Indians planned to bring them in one at a time in hopes of forcing the treaty to be made on their own terms.

But the foolish white officer had made a grave mistake. He did not know that the fierce plains warriors preferred death to capture.

"I will not stay here! I am going home!" cried Muk-war-rah. He flashed a hidden knife from his buckskin hunting leggings, and sprang at the soldiers by the door. One of them barred his rifle, blocking the medicine man's escape. The desperate Comanche plunged his knife into him.

Instantly, the whole room was in an uproar.

Soldiers' guns crashed point-blank into the crowded braves. The room was filled with choking clouds of powder smoke. The few Indians who reached the door were shot down by the troopers stationed around the Council House. Outside the building, their comrades, braves and squaws alike, ran for their ponies. Again and again, the soldiers' rifles thundered into them.

When the last round was fired, the pall of gunsmoke drifted away. A terrible stillness lay over the dusty Plaza of old San Antonio.

Huddled against the bullet-riddled walls of the Council House, twenty-seven red survivors waited.

All the rest, including three unarmed women and two small children, lay where they had fallen. Not a solitary Comanche had escaped that deadly ring of rifle steel. Thirty-five Indians had died in less than fifteen minutes.

An unwounded squaw was selected from among the terrified prisoners. She was provided with a swift pony and told to go home and tell her people what had happened. She was also to warn them that all the rest of the white captives must be brought in at once. The alternative would be war to the last Comanche.

The squaw understood. She said that she would do as she had been told, and that she would return in four days.

She was never seen again.

But her fellow Comanches were.

The time was six months later, August 8, 1840. The place, Linnville, a sleepy little gulfport town on the Texas coast. The players, 700 enraged red warriors. Their purpose, merciless, no-quarter revenge for the murder of their chiefs in the Council House Massacre. The password was, *"pei-da Ta'kae-kih!"* Translated, this meant "Death to the White Man!"

7

Comanche Vengeance

It was hot that peaceful August morning in Linnville. In front of his dry goods store, old Avery Hudspeth mopped his brow and listened to the big-eyed ranch boy who had just ridden his lathered pony into town.

Young Tobin Rhodes was beside himself with excitement. On his way into town he had seen, far out on the western plain, a tremendous caravan of Mexican traders bound for Linnville. Their column stretched for half a mile. There were hundreds of them, maybe a thousand. Maybe more. Tobin Rhodes had not stopped to count them, or to wait for them to draw near. It was not every day a boy of twelve got to wake up the town with such wonderful news.

But old Avery Hudspeth had lived a long time in Texas. A thousand Mexicans coming to trade with three hundred dirt-poor whites? It did not make sense to the old man. He would have to have a closer look before he believed that.

He hurried into the store and got out his ancient brassbound telescope. It was the one he used every day to watch hopefully for new ships entering Linnville's little bay from the Gulf of Mexico. It was a mighty stout and trusty glass. It would surely let a man see what was really under that big dust cloud, now clearly visible two miles to the west.

Thirty seconds later Avery Hudspeth had the venerable spyglass focused on the prairie. And five seconds after that his squinting eye popped wider than the three-inch lens through which it was staring.

He saw an unbelievable cavalcade of savage horsemen. There were hundreds and hundreds of painted braves. Not only that, there were blanketed squaws, with tiny babes on cradleboards strapped to their mothers' dark-skinned backs. The whole war strength of the Comanche Nation! They were hundreds of miles inside the western frontier! *And coming at a breakneck*

The Comanches looted homes, stores, and warehouses

*gallop straight down upon the sleeping town of Linn-
ville!*

"Injuns!" Avery gasped to the startled boy. "A
whole ringtailed passel of 'em!"

He dropped the glass and wheeled upon the frightened youth.

"Boy!" he shouted. "You git back on that pony of
yours and ride fer your life! Down the street! Git to
Major Watts at the custom house. Yell your lungs out
on the way. Them's Comanches comin' out yonder,
young un! And they're comin' fer us!"

Young Tobin Rhodes leaped on his pony. He knew
it was not only his own life he rode for, but the life
of every one of Linnville's innocent citizens.

Nobody remembers Tobin Rhodes today. They
should. In the ten minutes it took the ungainly Comanche column to cover the two miles to town, he spread
the alarm swiftly and well. Almost the entire population was able to flee to the safety of the bay.

There, they were taken aboard the cargo lighter of
a trading schooner lying offshore at anchor. From the
dangerously crowded decks of the leaky barge, they
watched in speechless horror as the Indians engulfed
the town.

They saw with their own eyes the death of gallant
Major Watts, who had lingered too long in seeing that
every woman and child was safely out of the settle-

ment. Then, throughout the endless hours of the blazing August sun, they watched in helpless agony as the savages looted their homes, stores and warehouses.

When nightfall came at last, no structure in sight had been spared. Everything of value which could be carried off on horseback had been removed and piled aboard the Comanche pack animals.

Nor was that all.

Between dusk of August 8th, and dawn of the 9th, the Comanche horde fired and burned to the ground every building in Linnville, Texas.

Stern proud men wept aboard the darkened barge. Their womenfolk prayed aloud and their little children cried piteously in the summer blackness.

When the next morning's sun rose sick and smoke-gray through the pall of wood ash, the Indians were gone. In less than twenty-four hours they had blotted out forever an entire city from the map of Texas.

Legend has it that the Comanches killed thirty-five white people on their way to Linnville—exactly the number of their chiefs and headmen slain in the Council House Massacre. The legend goes on to say that they took captive no more nor less than twenty-seven Texans —precisely the same number the soldiers had seized in San Antonio.

Hard fact places the dead at twenty-five, the prisoners at thirteen.

But frontier history is never too reliable. The fable is frequently as accurate as the fact.

In the case of the bloody Linnville Raid, the legend holds one dark advantage. For it was the way a merciless Comanche mind would have conceived and executed such a violent crime: an eye for an eye, a tooth for a tooth, one white man's scalp for every Indian man, woman and child who died in the soldiers' trap at San Antonio.

In the end, only two singular and important historical facts stand out about Linnville.

It was the first mass Indian raid ever conducted so deep into the white settlements of Texas.

And it was the last.

The Texas Rangers saw to that!

8

Plum Creek and Ben McCulloch's Ride

One reason alone had allowed the vast Comanche column to strike hundreds of miles inside the western frontier without challenge—and very nearly without discovery.

Their scouts and outriders, coursing swiftly in advance of the motley horde, surprised and shot down every living soul in its way. Thus the Indian leaders were satisfied that not a single white Texan had escaped ahead of them to warn the settlements.

They were right. None had. But what about the white Texans behind them? Indianlike, they had never thought of that. It was their first great mistake.

On August 5th, a lone mail carrier, riding from Austin to Gonzales, crossed the Comanches' broad trail near Plum Creek. He took one scalp-tingling look at the thousands of unshod pony tracks and spurred on to Gonzales. As luck would have it, Ben McCulloch of the Rangers was in Gonzales that day. He waited only long enough to hear the mail carrier's wide-eyed report. Within the hour he was riding. Yet, already, he was too late.

When he and his twenty-four volunteers reached Plum Creek, the Comanche campfires were long cold. Grimly, the Texans struck southward along the trampled course of the great Indian cavalcade.

Meanwhile, Linnville was burning and the red raiders were making their second mistake.

Instead of scattering to gallop for home in small bands and by a dozen different trails—their usual custom—they set out in a body to return by the same route they had come.

By this time the whole of settled Texas was aflame with the ghastly news of the Linnville tragedy. Yet the all-important question went unanswered. *Where were the Indians?* No one knew. They seemed to have disappeared. If they were not found—and found soon —they would escape unpunished.

As usual, where no one else was able to do so a Texas Ranger arose to supply the answer.

Ben McCulloch and his men had lost the inbound Indian trail during a night of torrential rain. They picked it up again, near Victoria, only hours after the sack of Linnville.

At once, the tireless McCulloch, with three trusted scouts, rode on. Within six hours he was back, bearing electrifying news that spread northward from Victoria. The Comanches were coming! And they were coming as Ben McCulloch had suspected they would do. Straight back along the same bloody trail they had blazed in their death march to the sea! *And more news.* They would be nearing Victoria by sundown!

There was time enough for the desperate Texans to make a stand.

In instant response to the bold Ranger's warning, the hard-faced horsemen raced toward the little settlement. By late afternoon 125 men were assembled on the prairie south and east of town. Shortly before sunset, the great Comanche host appeared.

The waiting Texans were stunned.

Until that shocked moment, none of them had actually believed Ben McCulloch's report about the tremendous size of the Indian force. The oldest Indian-fighter among them—Captain John J. Tumlinson of DeWitt County—had never seen so many red warriors gathered together in one company.

The glittering line of their painted war ponies and flashing lances continued on out of sight beyond the distant curve of the treeless plain. The immense cloud of dust thrown up by their mounts and by the vast herd of 3,000 stolen horses they were driving before them towered a hundred feet into the wind-still summer sky.

Captain Tumlinson hesitated. He was in command of his and McCulloch's combined forces. The decision to fight, or to fall back and let the Indian horde pass unchallenged, was his alone.

The Comanches had by now sighted the little white party. A detail of red scouts dashed forward to make sure of the Texans' apparent weakness. Ben McCulloch, guessing their intent, tried to forestall it. Calmly taking aim, he knocked their leader out of his saddle at 200 yards. It was an unbelievable shot, but the damage was done. The scouts had seen what they wanted to see.

Wheeling their ponies, they raced back to the main

column with the gleeful word. There were only a handful of the hated *Tejanos* waiting up there! They could be driven under in minutes by the favorite Plains Indian tactic of stampeding the horse herd through them. The warriors, slashing in on the heels of the maddened horses, could shoot down the scattered Texans like crippled buffalo.

"Gather the great horse herd!"

"String the war bows!"

"Pei-da Ta'kae-kih!" Death to the White Man——!

Seeing the Indian preparation and sensing at once its deadly purpose, Captain Tumlinson lost heart. Despairingly, he gave the order to withdraw and let the Comanche column pass.

"McCulloch," he told his youthful second-in-command, "we have got to get out of here. They are too many for us. We will fall back toward San Antonio. Captain Matt Caldwell is up there with his army boys. We can join up with them and make a final stand together."

Ben McCulloch was a Texas Ranger. He had taken the oath never to retreat.

"You can't do that, Captain!" he cried. "We must charge them now, or we shall never see them again!"

"We will retreat," repeated Tumlinson. "We have no other choice."

"But you will never get to Caldwell in time!" objected the young Ranger heatedly. "The Indians will slip away and we shall lose them!"

"You have my orders!" growled the older man, angry himself now. "Tell your men to retreat!"

"I will never tell them that!" snapped young McCulloch. And he never did.

Calling his three best men to him—Alsey Miller, Arch Gibson and little Barney Randall, all of whom had scouted the Comanche trail with him—he told them what he meant to do.

"Boys," he said quietly, "we have got to ride far and fast. Captain Tumlinson is going to let the Indians go past. We have got to see they don't get away."

"What kin we do, Ben?" asked Alsey Miller anxiously. "I know you *Rangers* are six-toed wildcats in a Injun fight. But, shucks! Me and Arch and Barney are only just ordinary two-legged humans. What kin the three of us possibly do toward helpin' you halt a thousand fired-up Comanches?"

"Follow me and I'll show you!" Ben McCulloch laughed. "And on the way I'll show you how to be Texas Rangers to boot! Either that, or show you how to die almighty quick, tryin'."

"Let's go," said Arch Gibson with a grin. "I allow I always wanted to be a Ranger anyhow!"

"Me too," and Barney Randall shrugged his shoulders. "I ain't signed no long-term lease on life recently. What you got in mind, Ben?"

What Ben McCulloch had in mind was chillingly simple. It was to ride around the retreating Comanche column during the night, pass the Indians in the darkness, find Captain Matt Caldwell and the army troops before dawn, and tell them where and how to set a trap for the murderers of Linnville before they could slip past San Antonio.

McCulloch's three companions nodded silently. They did not have to be told what might happen if the Indians got past San Antonio.

Once beyond that point, there would be no heading them short of the frontier. They would be safely back in the trackless prairies of their buffalo-pasture homeland to the west. No pursuit could hope to find them there. And they would have gotten cleanly away with their Great Raid. When the other warlike tribes heard of that, there was no telling what terrible bloodshed could result. The Kiowas, Apaches, Cheyennes—all the violent High Plains tribes—might flare up and start on a war trail that would wipe out every settlement in Texas.

It was no idle nightmare. The Indians could do it. The Comanches had shown them how at Linnville.

"All right, Ben," said Alsey Miller, tight-lipped. "What are we waitin' for? Let's ride."

That night Ranger Ben McCulloch and his three brave scouts made one of the most daring rides in frontier history. Today it is all but forgotten. Yet when it was made that sultry summer night of long ago, its failure could well have changed the map of our nation as we know it today.

If Ben McCulloch had not refused to retreat with Tumlinson . . . If he had not decided to make his horse-killing ride to warn Captain Caldwell . . . If he had not succeeded in reaching the army troops in time . . . If he had not . . . But "ifs" were never the way of the Texas Rangers!

McCulloch did make his great ride and he did reach Captain Caldwell in time.

Just at daybreak of August 10th, 1840, he and his exhausted comrades dashed into the army camp at Seguin, Texas.

Caldwell, after a hurried conference with the youthful Ranger, decided to follow McCulloch's "hunch" and attempt to intercept the Indians at Plum Creek below San Antonio.

Camp was broken and the march begun at once.

That night the army troops camped at the San Antonio crossing of the San Marcos River. Next morning the forced advance resumed. The way now led along the desolate trail the Comanches had left coming into the settlements. All day long the march continued across a prairie still burning with the fires set by the raiders. Flying ash, dense clouds of drifting smoke and the stifling heat of the smoldering flames choked and blinded the weary men and horses. Yet that night they reached their objective. Camp was made on Plum Creek.

It was 10 P.M., August 11th. Only one terse question remained in the minds of the bone-tired men.

Were they in time? Had they beaten the red foe to the fateful crossing?

Again, it was Ben McCulloch and his sleepless scouts who rode out to seek the answer.

Then, in the smoke-filled dawn of the 12th, they rode their staggering mounts back into the army camp. The wildest excitement ensued. Captain Caldwell had his answer. His troops were in time. Ben McCulloch's ride had not been in vain.

The Indians were less than three miles away! They appeared to have no inkling of the trap into which they were riding. The battle would be on—the issue won or lost—within the next thirty minutes!

The white troops were now in command of General Felix Huston, who had ridden in during the night with a large body of Texas militia. Caldwell was a far more experienced Indian fighter. He watched the nervous general closely. So did Ranger Ben McCulloch.

As the Indian force rode suddenly into view, one thought occupied the minds of Caldwell and McCulloch.

Would Huston fail to charge at Plum Creek as Tumlinson had at Victoria?

Ben McCulloch decided he dared not wait to find out.

When the leading Comanche war chief spurred forward to incite his screaming warriors to attack, McCulloch's rifle jumped to his shoulder. A single shot echoed across the prairie. The war chief threw up his arms, pitched off his pony and lay still, a neat blue bullet hole between his glazing eyes.

Ben McCulloch lowered his gun. He turned quickly to Captain Caldwell.

"Well, Captain, there's their Big Noise quieted down. Reckon you know what to tell the General to do now."

Captain Matt Caldwell did indeed know what to tell his uncertain commander. Instantly, he wheeled his horse.

"Now, General," he shouted hoarsely, "is your time to charge them. *They are whipped!*"

Carried beyond himself by McCulloch's cool marksmanship and Caldwell's high excitement, Huston ordered the charge.

His command came in the nick of time.

The Indians were about to stampede their huge horse herd into the troops. Instead, the unexpected suddenness of the attack by the white men caused the crazed animals to break backwards—squarely into the startled ranks of their own red masters!

The result was an Indian shambles.

The cursing white riflemen shot down the hopelessly entangled Comanches like helpless, blind-running cattle. No quarter was considered. The merciless pursuit and point-blank firing continued until there was no living red man left within bullet-range or horseback reach of the Plum Creek trap.

When the last shot had died away and the summer morning stillness settled again over the sunlit prairie, seventy-eight Comanche braves had ridden their last war trail. In his official report General Huston stated that their huddled, sightless bodies were found "concealed in thickets, sunk in the river, or on the outer prairie as high up as the San Antonio road."

It was the Texans' greatest victory over the savage barbarians of the plains. The once-mighty war lords of the outer prairie were never the same thereafter.

For another eighteen years they would continue to be a serious threat to the western frontier. But there would never be another Linnville, nor a raid of any kind into East Texas.

Ben McCulloch never claimed any personal credit for the victory. Ben knew better than that. He would have been the first to have doffed his battered hat and proudly saluted the real heroes. They were that ill-paid, little appreciated, often vilified "band of rascals" with whom he rode to frontier glory for a dollar and twenty-five cents a day—the Texas Rangers!

PART 2

The Vaqueros

Question the Mexican thief and marauder
Why his respect for the great Texas border;
Question them all, these beaten-back strangers,
White-lipped they'll tremble and whisper,
"The Rangers!"

A. E. TROMBLY
"Texas Rangers"

⑨

John C. Hays, Savior of San Antonio

There was no rest for the Rangers.

No sooner was the red foe driven back across the western frontier than a new enemy suddenly appeared along the southern border.

It would be more accurate to say that an old enemy suddenly reappeared along that border.

For the defeated *vaqueros* of Old Mexico had never accepted the loss of Texas to Sam Houston's hard-pressed little army of rebellious *Tejanos*.

In March, 1842, General Rafael Vasquez struck

without warning. His troops slashed across the border
at the heart of the still-shaky young nation—San
Antonio. He seized the city within twenty-four hours
and occupied it without resistance for two days. Then,
just as suddenly and mysteriously, he withdrew his
forces and returned to Mexico.

Texas paid dangerously little heed to the strange
maneuver. It had been a bloodless affair, typically
Mexican.

Forget it, was the Texans' attitude. It meant nothing.
Texas had far more serious affairs to fret about.

But did she?

Vasquez would not have thought so!

His 72-hour expedition had been a deliberate trick,
a bold adventure to establish the possibility of a real
invasion. Today it would have been called a commando
raid. Modern military men would have known what
to fear next.

Perhaps the Texas fathers did too.

For it is significant that they sent a little company
of Texas Rangers to guard the threatened town, instead of the regular army troops.

Just as significant was their choice of a commander
for this tiny force.

For the first important time in Ranger history, we
hear the name of Captain John Coffee Hays.

"Jack" Hays was a fighting man from a fighting

family. His father and grandfather had served valiantly with Andrew Jackson in the Creek and Seminole wars. He was named after General John Coffee, Jackson's most able and belligerent lieutenant.

Young Jack came to Texas in 1838, looking for a fight.

He found it at San Antonio.

He was still only 25 years old at the time. But he had ridden four full years with the Rangers of red-haired Henry Karnes and fabled old Deaf Smith. He was ready for the test which history had in store for him along the Salado River.

Nor did he fear that test in the least.

And why should he?

Did he not have Henry McCulloch for his lieutenant? And young Ben for one of his sergeants?

The McCulloch brothers were fighting Tennesseans like himself. They had come west with Davy Crockett. They had missed that doughty hero's death at the Alamo only because they had delayed three days to visit in the settlements. With men like these, what Ranger captain worth his $1.25 a day could worry about a few thousand Mexicans threatening to take back Texas?

Certainly not Jack Hays.

At least not until September 10th, 1842.

On that day he heard that General Adrian Woll of

the Mexican Army had advanced across the border with a full-strength field command of cavalry, infantry and artillery.

No one knows how many men Hays had at the time. Beyond doubt they were fewer than a hundred. The only official record lists them unglowingly as "the few Ranger spies under Captain John C. Hays at post San Antonio."

Nevertheless, hearing of Woll's approach to the city, Hays set out with only five scouts to reconnoiter the Mexican column. His main objective was to ascertain the exact location of the enemy.

Woll, a professional soldier of European training, was not to be so easily found out. Under cover of darkness he divided his command, leaving the main road and advancing northward in four columns. It was not until daylight that Hays found the invasion force —drawn up in siege position, completely surrounding San Antonio!

The resourceful Ranger did what he could.

Waiting for darkness of the 11th, he stole deep inside the Mexican lines. He had to know the enemy's true strength before carrying out the bold plan already forming in his restless mind. Had he been caught he would have been shot without military honors as a common spy.

The prospect brought only a wry smile to the daring

Texan's handsome face. And the smile faded swiftly when he had completed his dangerous count of the foe.

Unless his Ranger arithmetic was wrong—and he had just risked his life to make sure that it was not— Woll had upwards of 1,300 men in the lines he had thrown around San Antonio.

The city was doomed. Jack Hays knew that. He knew, as well, what next he had to do.

With his five scouts he rode northward through the autumn night, spreading the dread alarm.

"San Antonio has fallen! Rally Texans! Raise the old-time war whoop! Gather at Bexar! We shall fight them at the Salado!"

10

Captain Jack Sets a Trap at Salado

In Texas of that time, the night-riding war cry never echoed in vain. The usual ragged volunteer army of settler-soldiers sprang up and came in from outside Bexar County. Nor, in that dark hour, did the embattled ranchers rally alone. That old war horse, Captain Matt Caldwell, brought down a force of 85 seasoned militiamen from "up country."

As senior officer of those present, Caldwell was at once elected commander of the 225 Texans who had gathered at Bexar. In swift agreement with Jack Hays's plan to "gamble all" on stopping the invaders at the Salado River, he ordered the march to that stream begun within the hour of his arrival.

General Woll, leaving a garrison of 500 troops in San Antonio, advanced on the waiting Texans with 200 cavalrymen, 600 infantrymen and a company of artillery.

The two armies clashed across the Salado in the early dawn of September 17th, 1842. The bloody struggle raged until merciful darkness brought a truce to allow both sides to retrieve and bury their dead.

The Mexicans had asked for the truce, but it was the Texans who needed it.

Their little force had suffered an irreparable loss late in the afternoon. Captain Dawson and his company of 53 men from La Grange had been cut off while trying to unite with Caldwell. Under point-blank range of Woll's artillery, Dawson had been forced to raise the white flag of surrender. The Mexicans had replied by pounding his position to bits with their cannon. Of Dawson's "fearless fifty-three," only fifteen men escaped to bring the sad word to the Texan lines.

In turn, the Mexicans had lost a greater number, sixty dead. But they had had 1,300 to start with. The Texans had had scarcely 200.

Sleepless at his campfire that night, Captain Caldwell wrote in brave desperation to the government at Austin: "The enemy are all around me on every side; but I fear them not. I will hold my position until I hear from reinforcements. Come and help me——!"

But there was no time to send help to Caldwell's men. And no need to do so. Captain Jack Hays and his Texas Rangers made sure of that!

"They can't take the kind of casualties our boys heaped up on them out there today, Captain," he comforted Caldwell. "You wait and see. Come daylight tomorrow, there won't be a single *soldado* left in that river brush yonder!"

Caldwell was not so sure. But Jack Hays knew his Mexicans. They were brave enough—brave as any man—but they were just like the Indians. Once they had had a good fight and killed a few of the enemy, they wanted to go home.

Two hours before dawn, Ben McCulloch rode back from a scouting trip with big news. "They're pullin' out, boys! Lock, stock and cannon barrel! If we don't step spry, they'll make it clean away!"

But the Rangers were never famous for dragging their feet. And besides, Jack Hays had a plan. He wanted to draw out, trap, and take the Mexican artillery.

"Get their popguns away from them, boys," he told his men, "and Caldwell will have the rest of them chased back to Chihuahua by sundown."

All the Rangers had to do was push Woll's rear so hard he would have to drop the artillery back to cover his retreat. A forgotten member of Hays's company, who sprang for his pony in response to his captain's call, has left us this picture of Hays at that moment:

"Captain Jack Hays, our intrepid leader, five feet ten inches high, weighing one hundred and sixty pounds, his black eyes flashing decision of character, from beneath a full forehead crowned with beautiful jet-black hair, was soon mounted on his dark bay war horse and on the warpath!"

Hays's strategy with the cannon worked perfectly. His men harassed and taunted Woll's flank so hotly that later the Mexican general is reputed to have offered $500 for the head of the "wild black-haired youth upon whom he placed entire blame for his defeat." More important, the constant Ranger pressure forced Woll to drop his artillery back exactly as Hays had anticipated.

What happened then is best told in the words of another of Hays's devoted men.

"At length the shrill, clear voice of our captain sounded down the line—'Charge!' Away went the company up a gradual ascent in quick time. In a moment the cannon roared, but, according to Mexican custom, overshot us. The Texas yell followed the cannon's thunder and so excited the Mexican infantry, placed

Every man at the cannon was killed

in position to pour a fire down our lines, that they, too, overshot us. By the time the artillery hurled its canister the second time, shotguns and pistols were freely used by the Texans. Every man at the cannon was killed."

With the capture of his artillery, Woll's retreat became a route. His "homesick" troops fled so swiftly that Caldwell's command completely lost contact with them. San Antonio was evacuated and abandoned as abruptly. By the time Captain Jack Hays and his powder-grimed Rangers rode back into its peaceful Plaza, the only Mexican soldiers left in Texas were those who would sleep forever on the lonely banks of the Salado River.

11

Bigfoot Wallace and the Black Bean

The story of Bigfoot Wallace and the black bean has become a Texas legend, and it is herein given as such without apology.

Shortly after the Battle of Salado, Sam Houston had an idea. Since Hays and Caldwell had "so handily whipped the arrogant Woll," why not return the enemy favor and invade Mexico?

Houston was now in his second term as President of the Republic of Texas. He was undoubtedly a remarkable man, maybe even a great one. But he made many a wild and wonderful blunder in his time. He never made a better one than the so-called "Mier Expedition," the story of which follows.

In November, 1842, General Somervell, acting under Houston's orders, led the Texas troops out of San Antonio. With him, as "scouts and spies," went Jack Hays's company of trusted Rangers.

The makeshift force moved across the Rio Grande into Mexico, and seized the town of Guerrero. With the easy victory, Somervell's ragtag troops got out of hand. Shortly, looting and rioting through the streets of Guerrero, they were completely beyond Sommervell's command.

The General got scared; Jack Hays became disgusted. Both men quit the expedition and went home. Hays headed for San Antonio, taking his Rangers with him.

But the story of the black bean was only getting started.

Colonel William S. Fisher, the same officer who had ordered the Comanche Massacre at Council House, took command of the troops who refused to follow Hays and Somervell back to Texas. He loudly announced that he would lead them on to undying glory.

Well, he led plenty of them to glory, all right. But it was scarcely of the "undying" variety.

Among the 300 "unprincipled rascals" who decided

to accompany him into Mexico were four later-to-be-come-famous Rangers. These were Ewan Cameron, William Eastland, Sam Walker, and the good-natured giant who was to build a deathless legend out of an ordinary bean—Bigfoot Wallace.

We are told that Bigfoot was "the better part of seven feet tall." And that he "weighed twenty pounds less than a grizzly b'ar." "A size-fourteen shoe," we are asked to believe, "would not begin to encase his monstrous pedal extremities." The legend goes on to claim that he "spent twenty years killing Indians to find one with feet big enough that he could wear his moccasins."

It was just as well that Bigfoot was a sizable man. History had a sizable job cut out for him.

When Fisher's rebellious army reached Mier, which was no more than a miserable huddle of adobe shacks set in a desert of hot sun and little water, disaster struck. A Mexican cavalry regiment ambushed the Texans. Fisher was sorely wounded and forced to surrender. Every one of his men was captured.

They were marched 200 miles on foot, due south, to Saltillo, then another 100 miles west to Hacienda Salado. There they were imprisoned in an old military barracks. Their suffering was intense. Some of the weaker among them did not survive the blistering heat and thirst of the terrible trek. Those who did were in

The captured Texans were forced to march 300 miles

little better luck, for no prisoner had ever escaped from Hacienda Salado.

But the Mexicans had never had anybody like Bigfoot Wallace penned up there. Bigfoot was determined to show them that, and "purty durn sudden," according to his own account.

At sunrise, February 11th, 1843, he and his three fellow Rangers led the prison break. The war-whooping Texans overwhelmed the Mexican cavalry guard and set out across the desert for the Rio Grande. But even Bigfoot could not lead them across that barren waste. Crazed with thirst, many of them blinded by the merciless glare of the sun, the fugitives were recaptured by the pursuing cavalry and returned to Hacienda Salado in irons.

Here, Santa Anna, the cruel Mexican dictator, ordered that every tenth man among them was to be led out and executed. The manner in which those who were to die would be chosen was entirely heartless.

There were 176 survivors. Into a pottery cooking vessel with a small neck were placed 159 white beans and 17 black ones. The men who drew the black beans would be shot.

The drawing began. When its agony was over, seventeen of Fisher's troops had the black beans. The four Rangers found themselves with white beans. It was

in that moment of chill silence that the legend of Bigfoot and the black bean was born. No amount of historical evidence, not even Bigfoot's own honorable
denial, has been able to destroy it since.

"Boys," the legend quotes the drawling giant, "I
got here a perfectly good white bean. Now, I never
did cotton to pale-faced *frijoles,* and I will gladly trade
it to any of you who have got a black one."

There was a proud moment, then, for generations
of Texans yet to come. Not a single one of the seventeen doomed men would surrender his black bean. To
a man, they kept them and marched out to meet their
deaths "grim-faced but unafraid."

Bigfoot and the other white-bean holders were
marched deeper into Mexico. There they were man-
acled and thrown into the deepest dungeons of Perote
Prison. For many months they lay there, "rotting away
with disease and kept in conditions of the most un-
speakable filth." Eventually, all who survived were
liberated and made their various ways back to Texas.
Later, many of them, Bigfoot and Sam Walker in particular, returned and wreaked a terrible vengeance in
the Mexican War. But for the purposes of this story,
their adventure ended with the drawing of the beans
at Hacienda Salado.

That drawing, and the events which led up to it,

were important because they re-established two Ranger fundamentals which were, henceforth, to become the *living* heart of the Texas Ranger tradition:

(1) Like Bigfoot Wallace, a Ranger must always be ready to offer his life for a comrade's.

(2) Unlike Colonel Fisher, a Ranger must never again surrender to the enemy.

Fact or fable, the legend of Bigfoot Wallace and the black bean gave the famous captains of the Rangers who were yet to come something against which to compare their own courage and unselfish loyalty.

How well they served the memory of old Bigfoot will swiftly be seen.

12

The Rangers "Win" the Mexican War

For the next four years the Rangers, spearheaded by Jack Hays's San Antonio company, ruled the border with "fleet pony and ever-ready pistol."

In this hard-riding time Hays rose to be a colonel, the reward for his distinguished service in the defense of Texas lives and property against the continually raiding *vaqueros* of Old Mexico.

His methods in dealing with the border bandits, merciless by present-day standards, must be judged in the warlike light of his own times. It has been estimated that in that one four-year period alone, no less than a hundred Mexican nationals were "done in" by the border patrol. And this against the loss of "scarcely a single Ranger."

Hays had his grim reason for these summary executions. If his Rangers gained a feared name for never bringing in a live prisoner, hard necessity molded their lack of mercy. One successful theft of Texas livestock which was unpursued, or a single cabin-burning or ranch attack which went unpunished, was simply an open invitation to the next border violation.

Jack Hays left very few such invitations lying around his part of Texas.

Then, in 1846, the service of the Rangers to Texas was interrupted by their enthusiastic tour of duty with General Zachary Taylor's United States troops in the invasion of Mexico. Texas was a member of the Union now, and "Uncle Sam" was tired of the constant petty warfare going on along the Rio Grande. Furthermore, the greedy fathers in Washington were looking for a good excuse to "take a run down to Monterrey"—in short, to start a war with Mexico. The trouble in the brand-new state of Texas looked like a ready-made reason for this reprehensible undertaking.

Little difficulty was encountered in raising the war whoop among the Rangers. The memories of Hacienda Salado and the black bean were still fresh in many a

free-booting mind like Bigfoot Wallace's and handsome young Sam Walker's. A chance to chase Mexicans
under license from the United States Government?
With regular pay to boot? And plenty of good government food? Not to mention the bonus issue of two of
Sam Colt's great new six-shooters to each and every
man?

It was too much for the border warriors. Perhaps
they were growing a mite weary of their little war on
the Rio Grande. More likely, it was the promise of the
new Colts. They were the ones that Sam Walker had
been sent up north to have made to Ranger order. They
were twice as big as the old ones. They shot three times
as hard, and could be reloaded on horseback at a full
gallop. No question about it, a man could kill a lot of
Mexicans with a gun like that!

For whatever reason, the Rangers flocked into Taylor's camp. With them came hundreds and hundreds
of their wild-riding Texas friends, eager to enlist as
Rangers. Some accounts claim that as many as 2,000
men were in the motley "scout corps" which made up
Hays's regiment of Texas Rangers. A more acceptable
estimate places the number at 1,000.

Regardless of their true strength, the Rangers took
over the war as their personal, private expedition from
the very first.

Hays's men, and those of his two principal lieutenants, Captains Ben McCulloch and Sam Walker, led the attack in every major battle from Matamoros to Mexico City. In the crucial assault on the "terrible fortress" of the Bishop's Palace at Monterrey—the victory which marked the beginning of the end for the Mexican Army—Hays's frontier fighters won the day singlehanded.

Ordered to take the palace, which was the key to the whole defense, Hays stormed it in the face of the "most galling and withering fire imaginable."

Watching the crazy courage of the action through a spyglass on a distant hill, General Worth, who was supposed to be directing the attack, is said to have shouted impulsively, "By the Lord! Hays and those men of his are the best light troops in the world!" A veteran American newspaperman who was much nearer the action reported it better. "The Texas Rangers," he wrote tersely, "are the most desperate set of fighting men I have ever seen."

Later, when Hays's Rangers rode into the fallen capital, Mexico City, three more memorable pictures of them were drawn for posterity.

The first was by a foreign lady resident, writing to a friend in the United States. ". . . . Perhaps," the good woman suggests, "you would like to know who these terrifying beings are. Well, they are nothing more or less than Jack Hays and his Texas Rangers.

Rangers rode into the fallen capital, Mexico City

"With their old-fashioned, maple-stock rifles lying across their saddles, the butts of two large pistols sticking out of their holsters, and a pair of those new Colt's revolvers around their waists, they are armed with *fifteen* shots to the man! There are a thousand men in their regiment so they have 15,000 rounds which they can discharge in from eight to ten minutes when on the charge!

"The Mexicans believe the Texans are only semi-civilized—half man and half devil, along with a mixture of mountain lion and snapping turtle. They have more holy horror of them than they have of the Evil Saint himself!"

One of Taylor's highest-ranking generals wrote:

"Hays' Rangers have come. Their appearance is never to be forgotten. They are not in any sort of uniform, but are well mounted and doubly armed. Each man has two Colt's revolvers besides ordinary pistols, a sword, and every man a rifle. They affect all sorts of coats, blankets and headgear. The Mexicans are terribly afraid of them."

A member of their own corps, little known at the time but destined to win wide fame in the very next chapter of his gallant company's saga, stated with typical Ranger modesty: "Our entrance into the City of Mexico produced a sensation among the inhabitants. The greatest curiosity prevailed to get a glimpse at *'Los Diablos Tejanos'*—'The Texas Devils.'"

The pertinent similarity of these three greatly separated viewpoints is their common mention of the Mexicans' fearful respect of the Texas Rangers.

This fear was clearly very real. It must have stemmed from the four years Jack Hays and his intrepid fellow captains rode merciless herd on the "brown-skinned bandits of the border." And, beyond any doubt, it contributed greatly to the early defeat of the Mexican troops. If the "Texas Devils" themselves did not actually win the war, the Mexican people's fear of them almost certainly did.

As usual, an old Ranger has said it best: "I reckon we didn't start the Mexican trouble and mebbe we didn't finish it. But we sure raised up the middle of it higher than a dog-chased cat's back!"

The Mexican War was not a proud chapter in our nation's history. The part the Texas Rangers played in it can best be quietly forgotten. The unfortunate affair is important to the Ranger story only because it set the stage for bitter enemy reprisals on Texas itself, and because it served as a dangerous training ground for the rise of the next great Ranger captain, who was fated to deal with those reprisals.

He was a man few historians outside of Texas know to this day, but a man for all loyal riders of the hundred-year-old Texas Ranger trail to remember for at least another century.

His name was Major John S. "Rip" Ford.

13

Rip Ford and the Ten-Year Wait

Rip Ford was a patient man. It was a good thing he was. He had to wait a long time for his chance to join the immortal company of Hays and McCulloch and Sam Walker.

For ten years following Texas' entry into the Union and the end of the Mexican War, the fortunes of the Rangers reached their lowest ebb. The reason was disastrously simple. For those ten years the United States Army had been trying to take over the work of the

Texas Rangers. But the Federal troops made a miserable hash of the job.

Along the Rio Grande they had fair success, simply because the Mexicans were smart enough to suspend their border operations until the war fever had cooled off a bit. It was when the army attempted to replace the Rangers on the Indian frontier to the west that trouble arose again in Texas.

To begin with, the Federal Government forced the new Lone Star State to agree to set aside a reservation on the Brazos River for the so-called peaceful Indians still living in Texas. "You provide the land," said the United States, "and we will provide the troops to keep the Indians on it."

Reluctantly, Texas gave in. Three reservations were established along the Brazos near the Army fort of Belknap. One was for the Anadarkos, Caddos and Wacos. Another was for the Mescalero and Lipan Apaches. And the third was for the Comanches. All this took a great deal of time.

It was not until 1857 that the Indians were even partly rounded up and settled upon their new lands. By that time it was clear that the Texans' original doubts about the whole business had been borne out. Only the really peaceful Indians had come in to the reservations in any numbers. These were such long-beaten tribes as the

Caddos, Kickapoos, Tonkawas and the like. A few
dejected Apaches and Comanches showed up, mostly old
men and toothless squaws whose fighting days were
over. The real troublemakers—Iron Shirt and his main
band of fierce, white-hating Comanche braves—never
came near the reservations on the Brazos.

They were far too busy.

Things were looking bright up in Comancheland,
thanks to "Uncle Sam" and his orders that the Texans
were to keep their hands off the "little red brother."
It was now the job of the Federal troops to keep the Comanche in line, and the United States Army let it be
known that it needed no help from that ragtag band
of rascals, the Texas Rangers.

The new policy worked to perfection for Iron Shirt
and his wild-riding warriors. They could raid the western frontier settlements once more, safe in the knowledge that "the Grandfather in Washington" would not
let the "Texas Devils" trail them down and kill them
for their depredations.

So the Comanches went back to work at once.

By the following year, 1858, Texas had had enough—
United States troops or no United States troops.

Governor Runnels reached far back into the records
of the Rangers in the Mexican War. The card he pulled
out of the dusty files bore the name of John S. Ford.

Rip Ford was given supreme command of the hastily

reorganized frontier battalion. His orders were right to the point: "Go after Iron Shirt and don't come back till you've got him."

Rip Ford did not wait for details. He gathered his Rangers and started north.

The Comanches, hearing that the Rangers were back in business, gathered up their women and children and got out of Texas. They fled across the Red River into the United States Territory of the Indian Nation, later to become Oklahoma. This had been their successful practice while carrying on their new war with the distracted Texas settlers. They would make a raid, burn, kill and loot to their hearts' content. Then they would run for the safety of the Indian Territory and the protection of the Federal troops who were stationed there.

But Rip Ford's orders did not say anything about stopping at Red River. They just said, "Follow any and all trails of hostile Indians. If possible, overtake and chastise them."

That was the kind of uncomplicated talk the Texas Rangers understood.

On April 29, 1858, Ford struck across Red River.

His scouts found the Comanche camp late in the evening of May 11th. The surprise attack was launched in the eerie gray daylight of the 12th.

The first group of buffalo-hide tipis was taken swiftly.

The Indians, supremely confident in having pitched their lodges outside of Texas, were stunned. Yet two warriors managed to mount their ponies and escape, carrying the warning to the main camp three miles away. The Rangers pounded after them at an unbroken gallop, but the Indian mustangs were too fleet of foot. When Ford's little force topped out above the Canadian River they saw "a tremendous congregation of cowhide tipis, literally aswarm with painted braves either already mounted or running desperately for their tethered war ponies."

The battle was shortly joined.

Ford's forces numbered perhaps 200. Of these, fully half were friendly Indian scouts of the Shawnee, Tonkawa and Anadarko tribes, who had joined the Rangers as they passed through the Brazos reservations on their way to Red River. These were brave and good fighters, as anxious to end the Comanche menace as their white Texan brothers.

Iron Shirt's strength has been reported as from 300 to 500 "war-age braves, beautifully mounted and heavily armed after the Comanche custom."

Iron Shirt was a very dangerous leader. Ford knew that. The Indian war chief had taken his name from a jacket of ancient Spanish armor which he had found and which he always wore into battle. The Indians believed

Iron Shirt fell, riddled with bullets

that this rusted vest of Conquistador chain-mail made their chief invulnerable to enemy bullets. So far, the legend had held true. Iron Shirt had never been wounded in battle. Rip Ford knew that his first act must be to destroy the Comanches' faith in their war chief's fabled invincibility.

There was only one way to do that.

Quickly, Ford turned to Doss and Pockmark Jim, his two most trusted Indian guides. "You must bring down Iron Shirt," he told them, low-voiced.

Ford's continuing words tell the rest of it with terse Ranger economy:

"Iron Shirt was followed by his warriors, who trusted their own safety to his armor. The sharp crack of five or six rifle shots brought his horse down. The chief fell riddled with balls. Our Shawnee guide, Doss, and Jim Pockmark the Anadarko captain, claimed the first and last wounds."

With their leader dead, the Indians still fought with savage fury but with failing spirit. Again, Rip Ford's spare words put it with the most merciful brevity.

"The Comanches would still occasionally halt and endeavor to make a stand. Their efforts were unavailing. They were forced to yield ground in every instance. The din of battle had rolled back from the river. The groans of the dying and the cries of frightened women and children mingled with the reports of firearms. The shouts of desperate men rising from hilltop, from thicket and from ravine, were everywhere."

The pursuit of the broken Indian army lasted until two o'clock in the afternoon. It ceased only because the exhausted horses of the Rangers could run no farther. In the eight hours of its bloody course, Ford's aroused

Texans killed seventy-six Comanche warriors. They captured more than three hundred horses and took but eighteen prisoners. Their own losses were two killed, two wounded. Ford's official report closed with the deliberately pointed postscript, "The prisoners were mostly women and children."

It may well be believed that they were. Certainly, there were no able-bodied warriors among the prisoners. Rip Ford's men had a forgotten tradition to rebuild. The Texas Rangers were riding again. Let the red enemy understand that. Let him realize that it would do him no good to surrender. Make him know that if he wanted to save his life, there was exactly one way he could do so—and only one.

Get out of Texas and stay out of Texas.

A second grim postscript remained to the destruction of the Comanche camp on the Canadian River.

The remnants of Iron Shirt's band continued to raid the Texas settlements. They did not believe the Ranger warning. Not content with their own villainy, they went even further. They prevailed upon some of the "good Indians" of the Brazos reservations to join them in their scalping and horse-stealing forays along the western frontier.

For the crimes of a few weak brothers who were willing to listen to the lying tongues of the untamed Comanches, every Indian remaining in Texas was punished.

The reservations on the Brazos were ordered closed. It became the unwelcome job of the Rangers to close them.

On June 11th, they began the odious chore.

By August 8th, 1858, they had completed it.

On that date Major Robert S. Majors, the Brazos Agent, wrote bitterly:

"I have this day crossed all the Indians out of the heathen land of Texas and am now out of the land of the Philistines. If you want to have a full description of our Exodus out of Texas, read the Bible where the children of Israel crossed over the Red Sea."

Thus, the final end of the Indian in Texas. From that day no red man had any legal business in the Lone Star State. He was an outlaw and the Texans were determined to treat him as such. The Rangers were given orders to shoot him on sight, and no questions asked. A few pathetic bands continued to test those orders to their unvarying sorrow. At last, no more warriors came.

The red man's eighteen years' war with the settlements, so gloriously begun with the great Linnville Raid, was over. "God bless the Texas Rangers," sighed the good folk of Texas, and settled back to enjoy the first real peace they had known since 1836.

But they did not settle very far. They had turned their backs on the Rio Grande. It was all that Cheno Cortinas had been waiting for.

He struck at once and without warning.

14

The Private War of Cheno Cortinas

Brownsville, Texas was the most important town on the Rio Grande in 1859. Its permanent population of over 2,000 was ninety percent honest Mexican and ten percent dishonest Texan.

The latter owned and operated Brownsville. They exploited their darker-skinned fellow citizens without mercy. They cheated them freely of their every right as equal-born American voters. The helpless Mexicans lost their homes, their livestock—even their lives—to the first Texan who might want them, and who could afford to hire a dishonest lawyer to steal them for him. The Texans had plenty of money and there were plenty of dishonest lawyers in Brownsville. The result was a legal robbery of the good Latin American citizens of the town.

Across the river, in the historic old Mexican town of Matamoros, friends and relatives of the mistreated American Mexicans began to mutter darkly of a new war with Texas. In Brownsville itself, the persecuted sons of Mother Mexico were more than ready to listen.

All they needed was a champion of their own race.

History had one waiting.

Juan Nepomuceno Cortinas was a self-made rascal of the most colorful stripe imaginable.

Born of a wealthy and honorable old family of the highest Spanish blood, he was a complete scoundrel from the start. Faced with every opportunity of culture and education, he refused even to learn to read or write. He had one burning ambition: to raise a rebel army and return Texas to the mother country.

An account of the times describes him at the moment fate tapped him on the shoulder for his one-man war with the Texas Rangers.

"In 1859 he was living on his mother's ranch on the Texas side some six or seven miles west of Brownsville. Then in the prime of manhood, he bore a striking appearance. He was of medium size, fair in complexion, fearless in manner, self-possessed and cunning. His brown hair, green-gray eyes and reddish beard set him apart among his own people. He had inherited personal charm and acquired from his little mother excellent manners. These qualities, combined with a flair for leadership, the disposition of a gambler, an eye for the main chance, and a keen insight into the character of the Mexicans, made him a man of destiny."

"Cheno" Cortinas, as his devoted followers nicknamed him, did not keep that destiny waiting.

When the American sheriff of Brownsville seized his faithful lieutenant, El Borracho, The Drunkard, and threw him in jail, Cheno did not bother about seeing a lawyer to free his friend.

He just rode into town, shot the sheriff, broke open the jail and galloped off with El Borracho slung across the crupper of his horse.

Having won the opening round in such grand bandit style—the very image of a Mexican Robin Hood—Cheno struck while the simple minds of his admiring countrymen were still glorying in his daring rescue of El Borracho. Gathering a hundred cheering *vaqueros* around him, "General" Juan Nepomuceno Cortinas got on with his personal part in the history of the Texas Rangers.

At three o'clock in the morning of September 28th, the sleeping citizens of Brownsville were startled out of their beds by the thunder of 400 pony hoofs. In the next instant their pounding hearts were stopped by the wild cries of the invaders.

"*¡Viva Cheno Cortinas! ¡Mueran los Gringos! ¡Viva La República de México!*"

Hurrah for Cheno Cortinas? Death to the Americans? Long live the Republic of Mexico? What kind of crazy drunken talk was that in the middle of the night? It was not funny. The sheriff would hear about this in the morning, the inhabitants promised themselves. Steps would be taken.

But the sheriff had already heard about it. And he was already taking his steps—long and hasty and heading for the safety of the sagebrush. He wanted no part of Cheno Cortinas and his self-declared war on Texas. As a result, by daylight the little bandit was in complete control of Brownsville.

His first act was to lead out and execute three Americans who he claimed were "wicked men, notorious for their misdeeds among my people." Next, he broke open the jail again, freeing all the prisoners and declaring a general amnesty for "all helpless victims of the American lawyers."

For good measure and in the spirit of things to come, he sentenced the *Gringo* jailer to death—and carried out the execution with his own pistol. Then, seizing nearby Fort Brown, the United States army post, he tried hoisting the Mexican flag over its humbled ramparts. He failed only because the flagpole tackle broke at the crucial moment.

"Thus," bewailed Major S. P. Heintzelman, the army commander, "was an American city of from two to three thousand inhabitants occupied by a band of armed bandits, a thing till now unheard of in the United States!"

But Cheno was only getting started.

Returning in triumph to his mother's ranch, he set up military headquarters on Texas soil and issued his ringing call for revolution.

"We will not injure the innocent!" he orated grandly. "But we will strike for the emancipation of the Mexicans. *Our enemies shall not possess our land until they have fattened it with their own gore!*"

Hearing this, the Texans sat up and took sudden notice. This little man meant business. It sounded as though he actually intended to take over Texas. And not tomorrow, either!

A determined force of town militia, proudly calling themselves the "Brownsville Tigers," armed themselves with two brass cannon and set out for Cheno's ranch headquarters at Santa Rita.

Cheno, as promptly, gave them a good thrashing. He sent the "tigers" home with their tails between their legs, "a good deal more like buggy-whipped hound dogs than striped jungle kings."

Sterner measures were clearly called for.

Major Heintzelman started for Santa Rita with 165 regular army troops. But Cheno never slept. When the regulars arrived, he was long gone. The troops next heard of him in Matamoros, and Major Heintzelman did not like what he heard at all.

"Cortinas is now a great man," he reported worriedly in November. "He has defeated the *Gringos* and his position is impregnable. He has the Mexican flag flying in his camp and large numbers are flocking to his standard. He says that he will right the wrongs the Mexicans have received and that he will drive the hated Americans back to the Nueces."

Well, now what?

The Red Fox of the Rio Grande had whipped the Brownsville volunteers and run rings around the United States Army itself. Who could be found to hunt him down before his revolt got really serious?

Who, indeed, but the Texas Rangers!

In response to Major Heintzelman's thinly disguised yells for help, Rip Ford and 100 Rangers set out for Santa Rita.

Heintzelman and the army were waiting for the Rangers, but the Rangers did not wait for them.

"Follow us, boys!" Ford told the frustrated troopers. "But you'll have to step right along or you'll miss the main show."

Cheno Cortinas was a smart man. He did not trust the Texas Rangers as he did the Union soldiers. Away he went up the Rio Grande, Rip Ford hot on his retreating heels.

Three times the Rangers nearly trapped him, but each time the Red Fox got away. And each time it was because the Rangers were slowed down by Heintzelman's orders not to run away and leave the troops alone.

Finally Rip Ford had had enough.

Gathering his captains about his campfire, he said, "Boys, I think if we ride all night we can cut around this Mexican reynard and bring him to earth."

"What about Major Heintzelman and his bonny boys in blue?" asked one of his men, grinning.

"Let's not worry about them!" Rip Ford laughed. And away the Rangers went.

That same twilight, convinced that he was far ahead of his clumsy pursuers, Cheno Cortinas at last curled up for a good night's sleep. He picked a very poor evening to close his eyes. In the cold gray December dawn, he awoke to find the Rangers in front of him.

There was still a chance of retreating to the south. As Cheno considered it, one of his scouts raced in with some great news. The Rangers were all alone over there! The regular troops were far behind them!

Cheno at once saw his golden opportunity.

He had beaten the Texas militia and the regular army of the United States. Now he had the chance to wipe out a whole company of Texas Rangers. Why, the glory of a victory over the hated *"Diablos Tejanos"* would bring every fighting *vaquero* in old Mexico to his side!

Excitedly, he formed his troops for battle.

By this time, he had gathered a real army, complete with cavalry, infantry, buglers, battle flags and all—even a company of artillery! It would be a slaughter—600 stout *vaquero* troops against 100 ragtag "Texas Devils."

General Juan Nepomuceno sounded his bugles and rode forth with banners flying.

Rip Ford's Rangers were not impressed.

They charged Cortinas's center and tore right on through it, "with a withering fire of Colt revolver and single-shot horse pistol which emptied two-score Mexican saddles in the first sixty seconds."

After that, it was the old story of Jack Hays's Salado Trap all over again.

The Mexicans broke and fled. The Rangers war-whooped after them.

It was a good fight while it lasted, but it did not last long. "Within five miles we had captured all their cannon and had not a thing left to shoot at," remembered one old Ranger. Cortinas himself escaped into Mexico and lived on for many a fat year, according to the same informant, "practising his banditry on his own side of the river." But he, like General Woll before him, found a single taste of the Texas Rangers one large bite too many. He was never again caught on the Texas shores of the Rio Grande.

According to the old man quoted above, "Major Heintzelman and the United States Army came over the hill in time to get a southbound glimpse of Cheno's noble charger splashing out the far side of the river and hitting for the chaparral of Old Chihuahua. And that was how the army won the day at the Battle of Rio Grande City."

As usual, the army was not bashful about accepting full credit for the victory. Also, as usual, the official casualty lists fail to bear out the claim.

Sixteen Rangers died that day. Twenty-three were seriously wounded. Not a solitary United States soldier got a scratch.

It is very safe to say that Rip Ford and his Texas Rangers terminated the Wonderful Private War of Cheno Cortinas.

15

McNelly and His Men

After Rip Ford came the Civil War. And after the Civil War came the Reconstruction.

When the war began, the Rangers did what could be expected of such gallant fighters and desperately loyal Southerners. They flocked to the thirteen-starred battle flag of the Confederacy. They did so in such numbers that there were not enough of them left in Texas to make any Ranger history for the years 1860 through 1864. For the following ten years Texas was under the "enemy" rule of a northern republican governor. The Rangers were abolished in favor of a better-forgotten force of "carpetbag badge-toters" called the State Police.

Hence, until the spring of 1874, there was another "no history" period for the heroes of Plum Creek, Salado and the Battle of Rio Grande City.

Then came McNelly and his men.

They were not a moment too soon.

The Mexicans, under the old Red Fox of the Great River, Cheno Cortinas, had had fifteen years to organize a new kind of border war. This was the highly profitable hobby of running off good Texas cattle for quick, "no-questions-asked" sale in Old Mexico.

Cheno himself was far too crafty to get trapped again on the Texas side of the Rio Grande. But he had a reckless young lieutenant who lacked his leader's wisdom born of hard experience.

Guadalupe Espinosa was too young to remember the Texas Rangers. When he heard that they had been called back to duty, he shrugged. When told that they had been dispatched, under a boy captain, to put an end to Cheno's cattle-stealing campaign, he smiled.

He would have done better to have listened a bit more carefully to the name of that "boy captain," and to have taken a good hard look at his record before he came to the Rangers.

Leander H. McNelly had enlisted at the age of

seventeen in the Mounted Texas Volunteers. He had won a captain's commission in Tom Green's famous Texas Regiment before the Civil War was a year old.

At one time he and a handful of his troops captured 800 Union soldiers twenty miles behind the Federal lines. By the time he was nineteen McNelly was the most feared of the Confederate guerrillas operating along the Lower Mississippi. When he came home to Texas in '65, he was a glittering war hero—and just turned twenty-one!

But Espinosa did not bother to read his record. He was only interested in the fact that one twenty-one-year-old youth and eighteen Texas Rangers were coming to punish him and the great Cheno Cortinas!

Small wonder Guadalupe Espinosa shrugged and smiled.

Old Cheno had built up a band of a thousand faithful followers. He was running the biggest organized ring of rustlers the West was ever to know. He had waxed enormously wealthy doing it. And he was justly proud of his hard-earned title, "The King of the Mexican Cattle Thieves."

More to the immediate point: Guadalupe Espinosa had done such a noble job of stealing Texas cows for his greedy master that Old Cheno had just appointed him *mayordomo,* or general manager, of the flourishing "American Beef Company of Matamoros."

What had such a hero of the Texas-haters to fear from a thin, consumptive lad who had to affect a big black beard to make him look old enough to vote?

Under the circumstances it was a fair question. But the circumstances were due for a sudden change.

The name of the Ranger who brought about that change was Leander H. McNelly.

On the morning of June 12th, 1875, Captain McNelly and his eighteen Rangers, on patrol west of Brownsville, cut across an interesting trail. It was made by 250 cattle—undoubtedly Texan—and 14 horses, unquestionably Mexican.

"Well, boys," said McNelly, "I believe we have just found our first honest day's work. Let us get on with it."

McNelly was famous for his strangely soft voice. He rarely spoke above a whisper. Some said it was owing to his painfully shy nature. Others said it was because of his tormented lungs, already wracked by the tuberculosis he had acquired in the war. It did not matter to his men. They never listened to his voice, they always watched his eyes.

They were steel-blue as midnight stars, and had a sudden way of snapping like hot coals when he spoke. They were snapping now. Instantly, his little patrol "got on with it." They went at a dead gallop, straight for Old Mexico.

Within the hour, they caught sight of the thieves.

The latter had crossed the stolen cattle over a treacherous marshland and dug themselves in on a low hilltop just beyond the swampy ground.

It was a very bad place for McNelly and his men.

At the same time, the young guerrilla captain had been in far worse situations. He gave the famous old Ranger command without hesitation.

"Follow me, boys," he whispered softly, and plunged his horse into the morass.

A hail of bandit bullets cut about him as he drove his mount, floundering and struggling through the blue-black mud, directly at the outlaw stronghold. Behind him came his men, cursing and blasting back at the hilltop with their long-barreled Colts.

McNelly had not yet so much as *drawn* his pistol.

It was "too much *bravura*" for the Mexicans. Abandoning the cattle, they broke and fled for the border.

The Rio Grande was very close. It was almost in sight—just over the next hill. But McNelly had waited too long for this chance. At last he had trapped a pack of the swarthy rustlers on the wrong side of the river. There could be no question of mercy. And there was none. Of the fourteen frightened Mexicans, not one lived to see the Great River or to cross over it again into his beloved homeland.

McNelly himself, riding "like a dark angel" in advance of his men, drew first blood. Singling out the Mexican leader, he rode him down, killing his horse from under him with three revolver shots. Unharmed, the bandit leaped up and dove into the tangled brush of the swamp's edge. McNelly was down from his own mount in a flash.

Calmly pulling his Winchester carbine from its saddle scabbard, he walked straight into the dense thicket.

His Rangers counted six shots from the bandit chief's pistols. Then they heard a single flat crack of a .44-caliber Winchester. They saw McNelly stalk back out, his carbine smoking, catch up his pony and gallop on. There was no need to shout any questions about the Mexican leader.

They knew where he was—lying in that thicket.

They knew what he was doing—staring up at the tangled boughs with a Texas bullet hole between his wide-open eyes.

In the next few miles and minutes of the continuing chase, every one of his followers met the same swift fate. Within the hour of their apprehension, the last of the bandits lay quietly upon the Texas side of the Rio Grande.

Next, the silent Rangers caught up the escaped Mexi-

Awestruck Mexicans gazed at the lifeless bodies

can horses. Upon the nervous back of each was strapped the slack form of its late rider. Then the hard-faced procession set out for Brownsville, driving the recovered cattle ahead of it.

The sun was mercilessly hot in the Brownsville Plaza that day—July 13th, 1875. It stared down with a terrible stillness on the thirteen bodies laid out upon the baked earth of the town square for all to see and take warning from.

"Come and look upon the faces of your friends and loved ones," Captain McNelly invited the muttering crowd of Mexican onlookers. "If any relatives are here and want to claim a body, they may do so. *My Rangers are through with them.*"

His Rangers were through with them!

It was all the speech McNelly ever made about his deadly ride. It was all the warning he ever issued the stunned kinsmen of the lifeless *vaqueros*. And it was all the accounting he ever gave them of the thirteen corpses in the Brownsville Plaza.

It was enough.

The awestruck Mexicans understood it.

A dozen-and-one of their bandit brothers lay dead in the dirt before them. The fourteenth member of the band lay dying in the jail across the square. The young Ranger captain had said no word about who these *bandidos* were. He did not have to.

Those were Cheno Cortinas's men lying there, looking up at a sun they would never see again.

There could be no mistake.

The thirteenth body—the one with only a part of its handsome face still showing, a terrible rifle-bullet wound squarely between the eyes—was that of Guadalupe *"El Jefe"* Espinosa.

Beyond the silent bodies stood a row of motionless men in sweat-stained hats and brush-scarred boots. They leaned on their worn-barreled Winchesters, heavy twin Colts sagging their gun belts. These were McNelly's men, watching and waiting, their hard eyes searching the sullen crowd. Waiting, waiting——

But not a solitary volunteer moved forward to accept McNelly's soft-voiced invitation.

One man left quietly. Then another. And another. Within minutes the thirteen dead bandits lay alone in the fly-droning dust of the Plaza.

The free-handed happy reign of Cheno Cortinas, self-styled "King of the Mexican Cattle Thieves," was over. His long war with the Texas Rangers was at an end. For another four or five months the old man tried in vain to rally his scattering followers. He sent across a few more raids. Then, in late fall, when McNelly got good and mad and chased him right on across the Rio Grande into Mexico itself, the Red Fox knew the hunt was over. He retired deep into the Province of Tamaulipas, and was seen no more along the Texas border.

With the final retreat of the old bandit, the era of the border-raiding *vaquero* came to its colorful close.

Cheno Cortinas was the first and the last of his breed. After him, the others were only cheap imitators, and not very bright. The old man had been smart. He knew when to quit. There was simply no decent profit left in *Americano* cattle, for the Texas Rangers had raised the price too high!

PART 3

The Bad Men

The Comanche buck was fast to flee,
The Mexican cow thief faster,
But the lad who raised the mostest dust
Was the white crook following after.

He didn't run from the Sheriff's gun
Nor from fear of the Posse's danger,
He got so far, so fast, because—
Behind him came the Ranger!

ANONYMOUS

16

The Hunting of John Wesley Hardin

John Wesley Hardin was a Methodist minister's son. He had every advantage of a Christian home and upbringing. He was a bright lad, well mannered and quiet. He was kind to animals and very good to his gentle mother.

In fact, young John Wesley had only one serious fault in his character.

He was a merciless, cold-blooded killer.

The history and legends of the Old West have always been generous to the dashing bad man and brave bandit.

King Fisher, who was such a bandit, is still a hero in Texas. Up in Clay County, Missouri, to this very day, it is unhealthy to insult the memory of Jesse Woodson James. Tom Horn, another bad man, has become an Outlaw Saint on the Great Plains.

But nobody mourns John Wesley Hardin.

The West, old and young, has never liked a senseless killer.

Still, for all his murderous misdeeds, it is probable that John Wesley would have become a hero, too, if he had not made one little mistake, a slight error in judgment which had been fatal to many a better man before him.

He tangled with the Texas Rangers.

It was May 26, 1874. The town of Comanche, Texas, was mighty quiet. There was a good reason for that. The town had a good sheriff, whose name was Charley Webb.

At that time Comanche County was as dangerous a place as there was in the Southwest for a man to pin on a star and call himself sheriff. But Charley Webb feared no man, and certainly no bad man.

He was, moreover, a very courteous man. He never

failed to offer the hospitality of the Comanche jail to visiting outlaw notables.

When he heard that the deadly John Wesley Hardin had just ridden into town, he did not hesitate to do his civic duty. He simply reached for his hat and strolled down the street to ask the great man to be his guest while in the city.

John Wesley was at the bar of the Yellow Dog, Comanche City's toughest saloon. He was having his solitary breakfast of raw, red whiskey. It is safe to say that he was in an unsociable mood at best.

When the soft-voiced man came up behind him, he put down his glass but did not turn around.

"I want you, Hardin," murmured the mild-mannered newcomer, apologetically. "You're under arrest."

"Wes" Hardin had killed twenty-seven men, not counting Mexicans or Negroes. But no sheriff had ever put him behind bars.

He answered not a word to Sheriff Charley Webb.

He simply spun around and shot him through the heart.

Twenty-seven men had died under this twisted youth's treacherous guns. Yet their killer had still gone free. The twenty-eighth was not to join that pitiful company of the unavenged.

Sheriff Webb's deputy gazed down at the body of

the brave sheriff and asked himself a grim question.

If the state and local law officers could not arrest Wes Hardin, who could?

The white-lipped deputy thought he knew the answer. It was an answer to which frightened and angry Texans had resorted for thirty-eight years, and never in vain.

Webb's deputy wired the Texas Rangers.

Back came his terse answer.

If it took three weeks, or three months, or three years, the Rangers would get John Wesley Hardin for the murder of Sheriff Charley Webb. They would get him and they would bring him back to Comanche to stand trial at the scene of the crime.

At first, it looked as though it would be the lesser length of time, for within four months Hardin was captured in his Louisiana hideout and returned to Texas. But on the way to Comanche, guarded by local law officers and not Rangers, he escaped.

Patiently, the Rangers started all over again.

It would be a long trail this time. Hardin had learned he could not bluff the Texas Rangers. He would be very hard to find.

He was.

For three long years the Lone Star State neither saw the least sign, nor heard the faintest word, of John Wesley Hardin. The reputation of the Rangers began to suffer. Soon the situation became intolerable. Either the force "got" Wes Hardin, or it "forgot" forty-one years of fiercely proud tradition.

Lieutenant J. B. Armstrong was not inclined to be a forgetful man. He had received his early training under Captain L. H. McNelly. He had been taught to get his man, or die in the attempt.

Lieutenant Armstrong suddenly decided that John Wesley Hardin had "disappeared" long enough.

He buckled on his single, right-hand Colt and "went after him."

Right away, he ran into legal trouble.

There was a rumor that Hardin was hiding out near the town of Pensacola, in Florida. But when Armstrong tried to get the extradition papers that would let him arrest his man in that state, he was told that such things took time. He would have to wait.

The determined Ranger shook his head.

"You can bet John Wesley won't be waiting for any legal papers," he told General William Steele, the Texas adjutant general in charge of the case. "He will be long gone and far away, before ever you sign his extradition. *And so will I!* You tell the Governor to send the papers along," he went on to Steele. "I've got all the 'papers' I need to arrest my man right here!"

With these words, he patted the worn handle of

his old single-action Colt and set out for Florida.

The shadowy rumor was all he had to follow. It said only that Hardin had gathered together a band of "baggage-car bandits" over in the sunshine state, that he was operating under the assumed name of J. H. Swain, and that he was giving the Florida railroads a very bad case of hold-up fits indeed.

It was trail enough for a Texas Ranger. The Lieutenant followed it swiftly to Pensacola.

Contacting the railroad detectives on the case, he learned something very interesting. "Swain" was known to be riding a certain train that would arrive in Pensacola that very afternoon. Armstrong only smiled, asked the train's number and said, "Good day, gentlemen. Thank you very much."

At 3:45 P.M., August 23rd, Train Number 29 puffed to a halt at a lonely water-stop station just outside Pensacola.

A slender, gray-eyed stranger, neatly dressed and wearing a flowing imperial beard and leaning heavily on a cane, waited on the station platform. When the cars stopped moving, he limped painfully toward the steps of Coach Four.

The five hard-eyed men inside the coach looked him over carefully. Then they shrugged and went back to their interrupted card game.

They were sure none of them had ever seen him

before. Besides, it was obvious from his frocktail coat, ruffled white shirt and freshly pressed shoestring tie that he was a city dandy. He was also badly crippled and, more important to men in their hard profession, there was no one with him.

"Some Florida dude with the gout from eatin' too high off the hawg," growled John Wesley Hardin, turning away from the window. "Whose deal is it?"

Three years before, John Wesley had made his first great mistake by turning away from a saloon bar and shooting a Texas sheriff. At 3:45 P.M., the afternoon of August 23rd, 1877, he made his second great mistake by turning away from a train window and not realizing he had been looking straight at a Texas Ranger. For the slim stranger with the steel-gray eyes and the bad limp was Lieutenant J. B. Armstrong.

As he climbed painfully aboard Car Four, the Ranger shifted his cane to his left hand and drew his Colt revolver. A fateful moment later, "J. H. Swain" looked up from his cards into the gaping muzzle of a long-barreled .45.

To understand the incredible bravery of Lieutenant Armstrong in that death-still last minute when he entered Car Four, one must remember three things.

First, John Wesley Hardin was the fastest draw and deadliest shot in the history of frontier gun-fighting. No authority has ever denied that.

Second, a railroad secret agent and a Texas detective who were supposed to support Armstrong in confronting the gang had lost their nerve in the final moment. The Ranger knew they had already fled when he paused at the head of the car to draw his gun.

Third, the four desperadoes with Hardin were all wanted men, with prices on their heads and holstered Colts beneath their coats.

There was even a fourth dark fact weighing against Armstrong. He was still suffering intensely from an unhealed gunshot wound and could hardly walk without a cane. Now he pressed heavily upon it as he stared at the five startled outlaws.

That one man should willingly face such odds with a single weapon and the quiet command "Don't move; you men are under arrest" seems unbelievable.

But that is exactly what Lieutenant Armstrong did, and precisely what he said.

Wes Hardin knew guns. He knew more about them than any man alive.

When he saw that old model Colt with its seven-inch barrel and worn walnut handle, he knew he was not facing any Florida officer.

"Texas, by gum!" he cried to his companions, and went for his two .41-caliber Colts.

But for once his terrible guns failed him. His right-hand revolver caught and hung for a fraction of a second in his suspender strap. In the instant it took him to free the weapon, his seat companion leaped up, flashed his own draw, and fired at the Ranger.

Armstrong was now stalking slowly down the aisle, still not firing but determined to take Hardin alive. He fired back, once. The man who had shot at him screamed and dove through the glass of the car window to the platform outside. He ran five steps and then fell dead, shot through the heart.

Hardin now had his pistol free at last. But he was staring into the smoking bore of Armstrong's .45, not two feet from his face.

The Ranger, still intent on taking the outlaw alive, grabbed for his gun. Hardin lashed out with his boots, kicking his foe backward across the car aisle. Armstrong leaped back at him like a wounded tiger, slashing at his head with the long barrel of his revolver.

Blue steel met unbending skull bone.

John Wesley Hardin slumped to the floor, and did not move again.

When he recovered consciousness two hours later, the train was speeding through Alabama, bound for Texas. The outlaw's three companions had been captured without a peep and left behind for the Florida authorities. Lieutenant J. B. Armstrong did not want them. He had come to Pensacola for just one man.

He had gotten him.

"You men are under arrest," said Armstrong

That simple fact, and the rest of the story, is swiftly told in a terse telegram which General Steele was at that moment reading in far-off Texas.

TO GENERAL WM. STEELE   WHITNEY, ALABAMA
OFF. ADJ. GEN.   AUG. 23, 1877
AUSTIN

ARRESTED JOHN WESLEY HARDIN, PENSACOLA, FLORIDA, THIS P.M. HE HAD FOUR MEN WITH HIM. HAD SOME LIVELY SHOOTING. ONE OF THEIR NUMBER KILLED, ALL THE REST CAPTURED. HARDIN FOUGHT DESPERATELY,

CLOSED IN AND TOOK HIM BY MAIN STRENGTH. HUR-
RIED AHEAD THE TRAIN THEN LEAVING FOR THIS PLACE.
THIS IS HARDIN'S HOME AND HIS FRIENDS ARE TRYING
TO RALLY MEN TO RELEASE HIM. HAVE SOME GOOD CITI-
ZENS WITH ME AND WILL MAKE IT INTERESTING.

J. B. ARMSTRONG

LT. STATE TROOPS

John Wesley Hardin was tried for the murder of Sheriff Charles Webb in Comanche County, Texas, the last week of September, 1877.

The jury was out one hour.

The outlaw was found guilty in the second degree and sentenced to twenty-five years at hard labor in the state penitentiary at Huntsville. The gray iron gates closed behind him on October 5th.

Thus, the first and worst of the Southwest's famous bad men had been cut down to size.

And the man who did the whittling was a Texas Ranger.

17

Major Jones and the Frontier Battalion

The time was now the late 1870's. Texas was having a roaring boom. The reason was the great cattle drives thundering northward to the Kansas railways.

The cattlemen, big and little, were making quick millions. The beckoning smell of this sudden wealth reached eagerly waiting nostrils. From every outlaw hideout on the western frontier, all the way from Canada to Mexico, the hard-eyed knights of the calico mask and the Colt revolver descended on Texas.

The honest rancher had no chance.

The few sheriffs and town marshals were helpless.
The bad men simply overwhelmed them by sheer force
of numbers. Shortly, there was no law at all in the
outlying "cow counties."

The outlaw clan rode unchallenged.

Completely without fear of punishment, they shot
down those who tried to protect their property. In the
settlements, armed robberies of banks, business places
and private citizens took place in broad daylight, Mon-
day through Sunday. On the outer ranges, wholesale
rustling of horse and cow herds went on all night, every
night.

What happened next was inevitable.

The tax-paying Texan turned his desperate back on
the badly "buffaloed" local officers and sent, posthaste,
for the one true friend and fearless law officer who
had never failed him.

The Texas Ranger!

As usual, the Rangers acted fast.

They called in their famed trouble-shooting special
force, "the Frontier Battalion," under Major John B.
Jones of Corsicana.

The orders Major Jones received were in the best
Ranger tradition of coming right to the point. They
simply said, "Get out there and clean up those thieves."

Major Jones's response was equally to the point.

He got "out there" and went to work.

John B. Jones was the least-known, "littlest" Ranger of them all and, quite possibly, the greatest.

He was but two inches over five-and-a-half feet tall. He weighed no more than 135 pounds. Yet he had the heart of a lion and the spring-steel muscles of a stalking jaguar.

His hair, fierce eyes and sweeping mustache were as black as a bat cave at midnight. His whole attitude was one of such dangerous quietness and unquestioned command that no man who ever served under him thought of him as "small."

He was the greatest horseman the Rangers ever knew. His fiery bay stallion, Gold Eye, had carried him on more miles of risky frontier patrol than any Ranger before or after him.

Yet Major Jones was a far different man from his more famous fellow officers.

And therein lay his greatness.

Where Hays, McCulloch and McNelly had ruled "by iron hand and steel pistol," the little Major led by soft voice and superior cunning. In his long career as a Texas Ranger, he brought in more bad men than all his better-known predecessors combined.

But it was never the number he brought in that set him apart from his famous fellow Rangers.

It was "the way" he brought them in.

In his entire life as commander of the Frontier Battalion, Major Jones was never personally involved in the death of a single outlaw.

His was the highest art of the frontier peace officer —to take his man and deliver him *alive* to the proper authorities.

No law enforcement officer ever performed that hazardous duty better than Major John B. Jones in his dramatic clean-up of Kimble County, Texas.

On the day Major Jones received his orders, he and General Steele looked searchingly at each other across the adjutant general's desk in Austin.

When the latter finished speaking, Major Jones nodded quietly. "I understand the situation, General, and my Rangers are ready."

"Good. How do you propose to go about it?" asked Steele.

"Set them an example, sir!" replied Jones without a moment's hesitation.

From the beginning, Ranger tradition had been founded on that simple principle. If your trouble was Indians, get rid of the biggest Indian. If your problem was Mexicans, chase the Number One Mexican. If your difficulty involved American bad men, go after the worst one.

Major Rip Ford and Iron Shirt! Captain McNelly and Cheno Cortinas! Lieutenant Armstrong and John

Wesley Hardin! It was the way of the Rangers, and General Steele understood that. Still, he wanted to be sure.

"What do you mean, John?" he asked the black-eyed officer.

The little Major thought a moment.

"Which, in your opinion, sir," he asked, "is the wickedest county in West Texas?"

General Steele did not have to think before answering.

"Kimble!" he cried at once.

"Then, sir," said Major Jones softly, *"Kimble County is what I mean!"*

18

The Kimble County "Round-up"

The Rangers closed in on Kimble County in ten tight columns. The utmost speed and secrecy veiled their advance.

They moved only during the dead of night, camping under cover through the daylight hours. During the swift nighttime gallops no smoking was allowed. No campfires were permitted for boiling coffee to refresh the men after their hard ride. Not even a match was struck after the sun went down.

The result was a complete surprise of the bandit

gang, which usually had warning long beforehand of any law force's approach.

John B. Jones, the keen-minded little Major, did not confine his surprise to his approach, however.

For five perilous weeks, picked members of his company had been carrying out the most dangerous work in the Ranger service—serving as spies in the camp of the enemy.

These daring men, whose names are unknown to this day, had succeeded in upholding the established tradition of the force.

They had "gotten" their men.

When Major Jones halted the main column on the outskirts of the town of Junction, he had in his breast pocket a most remarkable list. It gave not only the name of every wanted man in Kimble County, *but the exact location of where he was living!*

Each of the other column commanders had a copy of the list. Their forces were poised, at the same instant, outside the towns of Bear Creek, Fredericksburg, and the other known outlaw strongholds along the Llano River.

The plan was to advance simultaneously, closing in on the courthouse city of Kimble. Here, District Judge W. A. Blackburn had a secret Grand Jury in session, waiting to indict the captured criminals.

At midnight, April 19th, Major Jones struck with

three columns from the southeast. The following day a second force cut in from the southwest. On the third day, their moves perfectly timed to catch the rascals fleeing the southern attacks, the remaining six Ranger detachments galloped down from the north.

The outlaws, caught flatfooted in their snug camps, broke and scattered like stampeding cattle. And like stampeding cattle, they were run down and roped by the night-riding Rangers.

If a man eluded one squad, he came squarely up against another. There was simply no getting around

Night-riding Rangers were everywhere

the widely spread Frontier Battalion. No least chance, whatever, of slipping through the shrinking cords of its ten-column dragnet. Rangers were everywhere.

For once, the outlaws found themselves outnumbered and outmarched.

Old men down in Texas (who heard the story from their fathers) will still tell you all about the "Kimble County Surround."

Major Jones had planned the whole thing, you will be told, exactly like a real Texas-size roundup. Only the little old Major was not gathering beef steers. No sirree! He was bringing in "bandit critters"! Popping them out of the pear thickets and the Llano scrub like so many mossyback longhorns, and herding them into the hoosegow corral down Kimble-way, peaceful and spirit-broke as any bunch of muley-cows on the way to the milking barn!

And he was aiming to slap a brand on them, too. One they wouldn't be forgetting the burn of for a considerable spell—*a big black Huntsville State Prison cell number, right square between their ornery shoulder blades!*

For ten days and nights the wild riding went on.

Every house was searched from root cellar to kitchen bed-loft. Every patch of river timber was beaten through by narrow-eyed riflemen, riding boot-to-boot. Every rocky hilltop was scouted out, every brushy draw flushed on foot. Not a square yard of Kimble County cover that would hide a grown man was overlooked.

The cringing captives were bunched and driven into Kimble.

When all the Ranger "roundup crews" came together there on April 30th, even Major Jones was astounded at the size of the "final tally."

He had started his historic "gather" with a list of forty-five names of known and wanted members of the notorious Kimble County gang.

When he checked his prisoners into the waiting jail, he found that his men had made forty-one official arrests. Of the entire listed number, and in a county bigger than some eastern states, *only four outlaws had escaped!*

Even more amazing action followed. The emboldened Grand Jury returned twenty-five true bills of guilt. And the charges were serious. Murder. Theft. Forgery. Assault. These were major crimes. They would mean long and heavy jail terms. These, in turn, would mean the sudden end of organized crime in Kimble County.

Major Jones knew that it was a desperate job well done. But the humble little officer would never have said how well done.

Fortunately, the official record remains.

In ten days he had arrested and imprisoned forty-one members of perhaps the most ruthless ring of organized rustlers and gunmen in Western history. He had done it in the toughest county in all Texas. *And he had done it without the shedding of a single drop of blood!*

It is typical of Major John B. Jones that he closed the affair by quietly denying his personal part in it.

"I cannot commend my men too warmly for their successful actions in this unpleasant service," he wrote. "The work of shelling the woods for wanted outlaws is extremely trying, as it has to be done mostly at night. No Ranger failed to respond at once and cheerfully to his duty. All credit is theirs."

As for the weary men themselves, it was all in the day's ride. They did not expect any credit for it.

They were Texas Rangers.

19

Sam Bass, the Ballad-Writers' Bandit

Sam Bass was a Yankee, bred and born in Indiana. Yet Sam gained his undying fame in the far South.

He was the only Northerner ever to have his name memorialized in the folk songs and ballads of the old Texas frontier. For, you see, in a twisted sort of way, people loved Sam Bass down there in the Lone Star borderlands.

His daring exploits outside the law, his quiet, friendly manner and the charmed life he seemed to bear, all combined to capture the Confederate fancy.

In time, he became a sort of Texas Jesse James.

Yet, actually, he was a very ordinary example of an entirely common criminal. His history is valuable because it demonstrates so clearly the dangerous ease with which a genuinely bad man can become, through mistaken sympathies, a popular hero.

And Sam *was* a genuinely bad man.

He was born bad. He grew up bad. He died bad.

In the simple songs and sentimental bandit ballads written after his violent death, he was invariably portrayed as a gallant Robin Hood of the Red River country. In truth, he was never anything more than a petty thief and a bungling, small-time outlaw. He was not even a good hand at his own hard profession.

Still, the folk-singers of his day insisted upon making a great man of Sam Bass.

So let us see what it took to make a bandit hero in 1878. Then let the reader decide for himself whether or not he would like to have ended up as Sam Bass did.

The tragic tale may even be told in the willfully favorable way of the old ballad writers of Sam's own time. The final grim point will still remain the same. Crime did not pay any better seventy-nine years ago than it does today.

The best way to prove that truth is to recount the first bad chapter of Sam's wild life by deliberately giving him the benefit of every doubt, just as his misguided admirers did so many years ago.

The purposely exaggerated beginning of such a story, told their way, would start about as follows:

Sam Bass was a great and noble adventurer, with the soul of a true Southern gentleman. It did not matter where he was born. It was the way he died that counted. And, like any brave and fearless son of the Old South, Sam died for what he believed in.

The only trouble was that what he believed in was robbing stages and banks and railroad trains.

Still, and no matter, Sam was just about the friendliest bandit that ever stuck up an express car or poked a big Colt pistol at a bank teller. He did his unpleasant work with a warm smile and a courteous word for every one of his luckless victims. If they smiled back and hoisted their hands, all went well. If they did not, Sam not only took their money but pistol-whipped them as well. That's how friendly Sam Bass was.

His early life alone held adventure enough for ten ordinary men.

A poor farmer-boy, he was orphaned at a tender age. He never went to school. Not young Sam. He knew a faster way to get smart. Travel, that was the idea. There was, he felt, nothing in the frontier world to broaden a boy like travel.

So Sam Bass took off from Indiana.

At a time when Huck Finn was still unborn in Mark Twain's imagination, Sam floated down the Mississippi River on a raft all the way to Rosedale, Mississippi. There, he lingered a year to begin his self-education.

What he learned in Rosedale was how to become the youngest cardsharp and crooked gambler in Mississippi.

Presently, he ambled on out to Texas. There, he taught himself a second shady profession. When he left to go back north (three jumps ahead of the local sheriff) he was an accomplished horse thief.

Never one to waste motion, Sam picked up another criminal degree on his way out of the Lone Star State. This one was from the College of Cow Knowledge. He lifted a fine herd of fat Texas steers and drove them clean up to the Black Hills of South Dakota.

By the time he sold the stolen animals in Deadwood, he could proudly call himself a postgraduate cattle rustler.

Sam was learning his bad lessons fast.

But he was hungry for more knowledge. In quick succession, he studied the high arts of saloon keeping, running whiskey to the Indians, and buying up gold mines. The latter were sold by sharp-eyed swindlers and were, of course, worthless.

When Sam found he had been cheated, he swore

vengeance. Things had reached a sorry stage when one hard-working crook could not trust another! It was time to learn something more profitable.

Sam had an idea where that might be done.

There was a weekly stagecoach that went out of Deadwood carrying Black Hills gold to the outside settlements. It looked like a paying proposition to young Sam. He gathered around him a little band of brother businessmen with no great respect for the laws of the land.

For the next seven weeks not a stage got out of Dakota with any gold on it. Sam and his industrious men made sure of that. In the process, guns went off and stage drivers stopped bullets.

Now Sam was an experienced gambler. He knew that seven was a lucky number. So after seven weeks he quit robbing stagecoaches and moved on. He still believed in travel, you see.

At Big Spring, Nebraska, he acquired another lawless degree.

With his trusty bandit crew he held up an eastbound Union Pacific train. Sam and his daring lads were in beginners' luck. The express company messenger was guarding a special shipment of freshly minted California gold. A few minutes later, the carefree outlaws galloped southward with $60,000 in brand-new twenty-dollar gold pieces jingling in their saddle bags.

Young Sam now figured he was well enough educated to go into business for himself. It was time to return to his favorite haunt, Denton County, Texas.

He liked it down there, always had. Besides, once a man has struggled hard to teach himself a profession, he has to settle down somewhere and practice it.

Sam had heard that new railway lines were radiating out of Dallas like spokes in a wagon-wheel. There were said to be a dozen of them, more or less. Surely a bright chap ought to be able to pick up a dishonest living from such grand opportunities—particularly if he did not linger too long between train stations.

Sam was right again.

In less than two months' time, he held up four trains within twenty miles of Dallas. Two of these trains belonged to the Texas Central Rail Road, and the others to the Texas & Pacific.

It was no trouble at all for Sam—no more trouble than it took to pull a gun on the express messenger and pack the gold pieces on a waiting pony. The getaways were all as clean as a hound's front tooth. The profits were every bit as handsome as a bay colt with four white feet. The prospects for steady work looked mighty encouraging.

Young Sam sighed gratefully and settled down. He was in business at last.

But Mr. Bass had overworked his illegal education.

Four daylight train robberies in fifty days were three too many for the angry Texas authorities.

The Rangers were called in.

Two days after the last job at Mesquite Station, General Steele wired Major John B. Jones. Steele knew the Rangers pretty well by this time. He did not waste words.

"TAKE CHARGE BANDIT HUNT NORTH TEXAS" was all he telegraphed Major Jones.

But by now Sam's outlawry had raised a hornet's nest of other law officers.

Word had gotten out that there was a price of $8,000 on his head for the Union Pacific robbery up north in Nebraska. Railroad detectives, Pinkerton operatives, United States special marshals and a hundred private agents, all eager for the reward, swarmed down upon Denton County.

Major Jones let them swarm. He knew how Sam Bass would have to be taken. And he knew that to take him would require time.

For Sam had showered around his gold pieces with gay heart and noble generosity. As a result, the grateful poor folks up in the tangled Denton County bottomlands, who had profited from Sam's big-heartedness, would shelter him to the death. He had at last become a frontier legend, exactly like Jesse James.

But even though the famous James boys had not yet been brought to justice, Major Jones knew all too well the only way to get to men like Jesse and Sam Bass.

It was not a pleasant way and Major Jones did not enjoy employing it. But he had no choice. He could not take unnecessary chances with Sam Bass's kind. He had to get to them in precisely the same way as he had gotten to the Kimble County Gang—*from the inside.*

The method Major Jones used to smoke out Sam Bass foreshadowed by nearly four years the traitorous end of Jesse James. And it worked the same deadly way. *He hired a spy to betray him.*

Jim Murphy was his name. And in Texas, to this day, you had better smile when you call a man "Jim Murphy."

Jim had been arrested for hiding out Sam Bass. He was a known member of the train-robbing gang. The Rangers had caught him and made him talk.

The traitor proved eager enough to save his own skin at the price of Sam's scalp.

In exchange for his freedom, he offered to rejoin the gang and warn the Rangers in advance of its next job. In order that Sam would trust him and allow him back in the bandit fold, a dramatic jailbreak was "arranged."

Sam Bass and his gang held up train after train

Next morning, all the Dallas papers carried the stirring news.

> Last night James W. Murphy, a desperate member of the Sam Bass gang, broke jail and fled. It is feared that he will find his old friends and that his warnings will prolong the chase indefinitely.
>
> Major Jones of the Frontier Battalion says that the incident is a downright calamity for the Rangers' long and arduous efforts to apprehend the wily Bass. . . .

It was a calamity, all right. But not for the Rangers.

Sam Bass fell for the deadly trick, hook, line and six-gun. Jim Murphy was welcomed back warily enough, but soon convinced the happy-go-lucky Sam that he was his best and staunchest friend.

His name, according to the old ballad-writers, should not have been Jim—it should have been Judas.

For Jim Murphy betrayed Sam Bass and led him to his death.

But with that betrayal, the work of the old ballad-writers is done. Their distorted opening chapter of Sam's short life is finished. From then on the Texas Rangers took over. And they were duly-sworn officers of the law, not sentimental ballad-singers.

Somehow, they couldn't see anything particularly great or noble about shooting down an unarmed bank teller in cold blood. Or anything especially brave or fearless in pistol-whipping an honest railroad baggage-man. Or anything outstandingly kind and generous about assaulting a poor ignorant stage driver.

Somehow, they just never did get the idea that Sam Bass was much of a hero.

So they were out to get him.

20

The Last of the Great Bad Men

For many weeks after his "escape" nothing was heard of Jim Murphy. Sam and his gang made but one brief appearance out of hiding, and that was for the purpose of stealing fresh horses for their next job. The Pinkertons and railroad agents still buzzed in and around Denton County as thick as hiving bees. But they buzzed in vain. Sam was not to be so easily stung.

The Rangers sat back and waited.

The other law officers began to grin and say that Major Jones had at last met his match. They liked that.

There never had been any official love lost between the county sheriffs and the Texas Rangers. The latter had had to come to their rescue too often. It made the sheriffs look bad.

Major Jones said nothing. He knew Jim Murphy.

On a sultry day in mid-July, the Major got what he had been waiting for.

It was a letter postmarked in Denton County. It was not signed, nor did it need to be. Major Jones ripped it open, his black eyes narrowing to steely slits.

This is what he read:

> We have left Denton. Sam, Frank Jackson, Seaborn Barnes and me. The party is again very suspicious of me, having once more been warned that I am a spy. I have had no opportunity to communicate with you until now.
>
> They are going to rob the bank or railroad at Round Rock, unless you get there in time to prevent it. If you don't come, I will have to help them, or they will kill me.
>
> I beg of you, in God's name, to be there. . . .

Jim Murphy did not beg the Lord's name in vain. The Rangers were there.

But first, Major Jones studied the letter.

It gave him very little time. There was no large force of Rangers near the threatened town. Jones himself was the closest to it. He was attending an outlaw trial in which he was a witness at Austin. He had only three Rangers with him.

Again he counted the names in the letter. Bass. Jackson. Barnes. Murphy. Four outlaws. He glanced up, counting his Rangers. Dick Ware. Chris Connor. George Harrell. He smiled softly, and added himself to the count.

Four bad men, four Rangers. Good enough. The odds were even. Major Jones and his men mounted up and rode.

They reached Round Rock on Thursday, July 18th, after a killing ride. Word from Murphy reached them that night. The outlaws were camped in the old cemetery outside town. They would ride in next day to look the bank over, then rob it the following day, Saturday, July 20th.

Major Jones decided he would not wait for the boys to take on another load of bright Texas gold.

If Sam showed up on schedule the next day, he would pick up a deadlier burden and a duller-colored one, composed of good gray Ranger lead.

Toward this end, the Major was forced to take two local peace officers into his confidence, for he and his Rangers did not know Sam Bass on sight. Deputy sheriffs Grimes and Moore did.

The trap was set.

Friday morning dawned clear and hot. The sticky hours dragged by. The dusty main street of Round Rock lay strangely quiet. Not a citizen in town knew of the nearness of the Bass gang. Yet the noonday stillness had an eerie quality to it.

The sun burned mercilessly on. High noon. One o'clock. Two. Three.

Still nothing.

Then, suddenly, four narrow-eyed horsemen appeared to the north. They jogged their lathered mounts slowly down the street. Each wore a long cavalry coat despite the melting heat. This was understandable, for men who made their living with cross-belted Colt revolvers did not advertise the fact.

Presently, the fourth rider stopped and got down off his horse. He picked up the animal's hoof and waved to his companions that he would be along in a minute. There was just a small pebble in the frog of his gelding's foot. He would have it freed with his pocketknife in no time.

His three friends nodded and rode on.

"Jim Murphy!" whispered Major Jones. Then, tersely, to the two deputies, "Is that Bass in the lead?"

Grimes shook his head uncertainly. "I can't see against this infernal sun. When they get down to case the bank, me and Moore will drift over and make sure, close up. Then we can signal you."

"All right. But whatever you do, don't jump them by yourselves."

"Lookit yonder!" interrupted Deputy Moore. "They're going into Kopperal's Dry Goods, next the bank!"

"Let's go," grunted the brave Grimes.

"Remember!" Major Jones's low-voiced warning came again. "Just look them over and give us the signal."

"Sure," muttered Deputy Grimes, and stalked across the street to keep his date with destiny.

In the store, Sam was laughing and joking with the clerk, Simon Jude. Jude later said he never met a better-natured fellow.

There is no explanation for what happened next.

For at the last minute, Deputy Grimes disobeyed his orders.

Perhaps he did it because of the $8,000 reward on Sam's head. Perhaps he wanted the glory of taking the great bandit singlehanded, or the professional satisfaction of showing up the Texas Rangers.

Two things alone are certain.

One is that Deputy Sheriff Grimes was one of the bravest peace officers who ever lived.

And the second is that he was also one of the most foolish.

He gave a warning nod to his friend Moore, and stepped up behind Sam Bass.

"I'll thank you for your gun, Sam," were his first —and last—words.

Sam whirled and shot him dead. Behind him, Deputy Moore went for his Colt. He got off one shot at Sam, nicking him in the gun hand. Sam flashed his other .44 and drilled a shot clear through both lungs of the second officer.

Then he said, "Boys," nodding to Barnes and Jackson, "I think we had better go. There may be more of them outside. Good day to you, Mr. Jude."

As usual, Sam Bass was right. There were "more of them" outside.

But the ones out there were not local deputies. And they were not trying to beat Sam Bass to the draw with revolvers.

They were Texas Rangers.

And they were firing point-blank across a sixty-foot street with lever-action Winchester rifles.

As the cornered outlaws ran for their horses, six-guns blasting, Ranger Dick Ware squinted coolly along his carbine barrel. He fired once. Seaborn Barnes spun into the main-street dust, a .44 Winchester bullet in his brain.

In the same instant, with outlaw lead splattering the

The outlaws were shot as they ran for their horses

adobe wall behind him, Ranger George Harrell laid his
sights on Sam Bass.

He could see the famous bad man's body jerk at
every shot. But Sam Bass was tough. Shot through half
a dozen times, he still managed to make his horse. Frank
Jackson lifted him into the saddle and held him there

as the two galloped out of town under a withering blizzard of Ranger lead.

The brave and loyal Frank Jackson was never found.

But Sam Bass was.

Early the next morning the Rangers trailed him to his last hideout. It was a gaunt, gnarled mesquite tree standing in solitary loneliness on the level prairie just north of Round Rock. Beneath its dusty shade, his shattered body braced against the rough bark, sat Sam Bass.

Texas' beloved bandit had halted his last train, robbed his last bank.

When the Rangers came up to him, he smiled weakly and managed a gallant wave.

"Don't bother shooting, boys!" he called, gray-faced with pain. "I am the man you are looking for. I am Sam Bass."

Walter Prescott Webb has left us the best picture of the actual death of the little outlaw.

"He was brought to Round Rock and Dr. Cochran was called to attend his wounds. Every attention was given him by Major Jones. Bass lingered until Sunday, conscious to the last. Major Jones was with him, or had others with him, all the time, and made every effort to learn from him the identity and whereabouts of his confederates. All his statements were written down. Bass steadfastly refused to give information, though he talked freely of the men who were killed, and of the facts that were well known.

"On Sunday Bass's death became a certainty. Major Jones again tried to gain some information.

" 'No,' said Bass, 'I won't tell.'

" 'Why won't you?' asked Major Jones.

" 'Because it's agin my profession. . . . If a man knows anything he ought to die with it in him.' And Sam did."

When Dr. Cochran told him the end was near, he said, "Let me go." And, as he went, he said:

"The world is bobbing around!"

Thus passed the last of the great bad men.

Many a question has been asked about the life and death of Sam Bass. The one which seems to tell his whole sad story the best appears in the last line engraved on a forlorn granite headstone in the old cemetery at Round Rock, Texas.

SAMUEL BASS
Born July 21, 1851
Died July 21, 1878
A Brave Man Reposes In Death Here
Why Was He Not True?

No man will ever know why Sam Bass was not true. But there can never be any doubt at all about why he was dead.

He just crossed trails with the Texas Rangers.

It was as simple as that.

21

End of the Ranger Trail

John Wesley Hardin was in jail. The Kimble County gang was wiped out. Sam Bass was dead. Thus, the gunman killer had been tamed, the cattle rustler caged, the bank-and-train robber cut down.

Before them, the other enemies of the Lone Star state had met as swift a fate at the gun hands of the Texas Rangers.

Ben McCulloch and his Plum Creek boys had whipped the wild Comanche. Jack Hays and his Texas Devils had helped win the Mexican War.

McNelly and his Iron Men had finished off the Border Bandit.

Now, Major John B. Jones and his Frontier Battalion had pretty well pacified the American Bad Man.

What real work honestly remained for the hard-riding Texas Rangers?

Well, one or two little odd jobs, anyway——

There was, by way of interesting example, the strange case of Sergeant Ira Aten and the Dynamite Bomb.

In 1874, barbed wire was introduced into Texas. By the time the bad men were brought to heel, the open range was being fenced in at an alarming rate. The hated "bobwire" was nearly everywhere.

In a few more years, it *was* everywhere.

And the embittered cattlemen were up in arms.

Looking about for a weapon with which to fight the "fence-building" homesteaders, who were wiring off the last of the great range, the big "free grass" ranchers found—of all innocent things—a pair of ordinary wire-nippers!

The Fence Cutters' War was instantly under way.

It was easy.

All an angry cattleman had to do was have one of his cowboys ride out when the moon was dark, and cut his farmer neighbor's nice new fence into forty-foot pieces!

The job was done in minutes and there was no evidence upon which to make an arrest.

The gunman could be caught with the murder weapon. The horse thief could be apprehended with the stolen pony, the cow thief nabbed with the rustled steer, the bank-and-train robber trapped with the jingling gold.

But the fence cutter?

He just threw away his nippers when the job was done, and rode whistling on his way.

That is, he did until the frustrated fence men sent for the Rangers.

And the Rangers sent the fence men slow-drawling Sergeant Ira Aten.

If the expression may be excused, young Ira found his work "cut out" for him.

He would spend weeks of dangerous spy work around the big ranches. To have been caught prowling these ranges would have meant the mysterious disappearance of one more Ranger in the line of risky duty. But Ira Aten prowled on.

Long days of careful detective work tracking down a certain bunch of fence cutters would be followed by endless nights of "laying out" along the threatened line of barbed wire, waiting for the cutters to return.

Then, while the patient Ranger lay shivering in

ambush on that fenceline, the cutters would butcher another line forty miles away.

Still, Ranger Aten was a man of boundless determination and of considerable inventive genius. After enough weeks of wasting his good time lying out in the cold prairie darkness, he had an idea.

Like all Ranger ideas, it was short and to the point. It aimed to set an example to just *one* fence cutter that would serve to encourage *all* fence cutters to throw away their wire-nippers.

To accomplish this, Ranger Aten took six sticks of dynamite and wired them to a particular fence which had been cut three times in as many weeks. From the bundle of dynamite, he ran another wire to the trigger of a hidden gun which was nailed to a nearby tree and aimed squarely at the dynamite.

The theory of operation was uncomplicated.

(1) Mr. Fence Cutter snipped the fence. (2) The released wire triggered the loaded gun. (3) The gun went off. (4) The bullet hit the dynamite. (5) Mr. Fence Cutter disappeared.

Content with his invention, Sergeant Aten sat back to roll a cigarette and await results.

Presently, on a fine dark night, there was a range-shaking explosion along the particular fence that had been cut three times in as many weeks.

Homestead windows rattled for five miles around.

In the morning the cautiously curious farmers went out to find out what had happened.

They did not find much. Just the singed brim of a powder-burned Stetson hat. A small piece of a cowboy-boot heel. The scorched seat of a pair of Levi Strauss blue jeans. And a fine new pair of barbed-wire nippers—slightly bent from having been blasted halfway through an adjacent fence post.

Sergeant Ira Aten said nothing. He just saddled up his pony and rode away.

The Fence Cutters' War was over.

Historians will contest the central fact of this fine Texas legend. Let them. Argue as they will over whether or not the dynamite bomb was ever actually exploded, they cannot avoid the all-important result of its ingenious invention: the Texas Rangers had won another signal victory against seemingly insurmountable odds.

Not all Rangers, of course, were as quick to understand a situation as Sergeant Aten.

There was, for instance, the case of Private Ragan Kenedy and his famous "fumigation by six-shooter" misadventure.

Private Kenedy was sent down on the border to fumigate a certain hut whose Mexican inhabitants had come down with a slight case of smallpox. His orders were not too clear, and neither was the simple mind of Ranger Ragan Kenedy.

When he was told to fumigate the hut, he assumed that the poor souls who lived in it were intended to get the same poisonous treatment.

The uneducated peons did not understand the science of killing germs any better than the big Ranger. When he told them to get inside the hut and stay there, they obeyed meekly.

But when he lit the deadly-smoking formaldehyde candles which he had been given for the job, the strangling family at once rushed back outside.

Orders were orders to Private Ragan Kenedy.

Whipping out his six-gun, he herded the choking Mexicans back into the fume-clouded hut.

Again they broke out, gasping for breath and clawing frantically at their burning throats.

Private Kenedy set his blunt jaw. Grabbing his unhappy victims by the neck, he literally dragged them back inside the miserable hovel. This time there would be no slip-ups, by jingo! To make certain of it, he would stay in there with the rascals.

Slamming and barring the plank door, the strapping Ranger stood in front of it glaring his defiance at the cowering occupants.

He did not glare very long. In fact, he led the wild rush back out into the blessed open air.

Not even a Texas Ranger could outfight a formaldehyde fumigating candle!

But Ranger Kenedy was big enough to accept his
failure like the six-foot Texan he was.

"I have fumigated the house real good," he wrote
his company captain apologetically. "But I fear as
much cannot be said for its inhabitants."

It must not be imagined that all Ranger work after
1880 was so simple or had such humorous results.

Such deserving captains as Lee Hall, John R. Hughes,
Dan Roberts and June Peak ran down many a hard-
case criminal and hanged more than a few rustlers
and horse thieves after this date.

The full history of the force covered almost exactly
100 years. It began with the Texas war for independence in 1836, and did not end officially until the following brief report appeared in the New York *Herald
Tribune* of August 4, 1935.

> ". . . Famous in tradition as the Southwest's most
> picturesque and most fearless law-enforcement group,
> the Texas Rangers as now constituted will pass out of
> existence August 10 . . ."

But the real finish had been written long before it
was announced in any big-city news item.

The romantic truth is that after 1880 the Forty Year War of the Texas Rangers against the fierce Comanche, the vengeful *vaquero* and the gun-toting outlaw was at an end.

The Rangers had won every battle, from the ambush of the Linnville Raiders at Plum Creek to the trapping of Sam Bass at Round Rock.

They had never taken a backward step to any wrongdoer, be he red, white, or brown. They had never surrendered. They had never deserted a comrade. They had never come back without their man.

But the Indian was gone, the *vaquero* forgotten, and the desperado peacefully at rest in his lonely grave.

A great land, comprising one-twelfth of the total area of the United States, had been made safe and its frontiers guaranteed forever by a little band of resolute men who were willing to offer their lives for an ideal— and who asked no quarter from any foe for the privilege.

And so, good-bye to handsome Jack Hays and smiling Ben McCulloch. Adieu to young Sam Walker and fiery-eyed Rip Ford. *Adios* to soft-voiced Captain L. H. McNelly. To fearless J. B. Armstrong and gentle little Major Jones. To sharp-shooting George Harrell and dead-eyed Dick Ware. To sly-minded Sergeant Ira Aten and slow-witted Private Ragan Kenedy, and to all the other big and little heroes who fought and died for $1.25 a day! Good-bye to them all, and to each a heartfelt "well done!"

Salute them now, as they ride proudly by, for their gallant kind will never pass again.

The gun smoke closes in. The clock of history has run down. The riders fade away along the starlit Rio Grande.

Farewell to the Texas Rangers . . . !

Epilogue

The Texas Rangers Today

Since the historic reorganization of the Rangers in 1935, the force has continued its proud tradition as an impor- tant branch of the Texas Department of Public Safety Including its exploits after 1935, to the present, the Texas Ranger Force is the oldest law enforcement agency on the North American continent with statewide jurisdiction. This is a remarkable record of uninter- rupted service, and it is to take nothing from today's Ranger to feel, as the author does, that his story rightly belongs in another book.

To compare the present-day Ranger with his shaggy-haired brother of a hundred years ago would be to compare Sergeant Joe Friday with Wyatt Earp or Wild Bill Hickok.

Of course, there can be no fair comparison.

Circumstances make men.

And the circumstances which made men like Jack Hays, Rip Ford, Leander H. McNelly and Major John B. Jones do not exist today.

Texas Rangers still serve in the hard line of law duty as bravely in 1957 as in 1836. The highways and byways of the great Longhorn State are admittedly the safer for the sacrifices of these twentieth-century descendants of Private Noah Smithwick and Captain Ben McCulloch. But our tale does not concern them. It deals with their forefathers who founded the force when Comanche trails wandered where four-lane freeways run today. We have tried to dedicate it, therefore, to the lasting glory of the oldtime Texas Ranger without detracting in any way from the splendid record of his modern counterpart.

All hail the Texas Rangers, then and now!

Few better and no braver men have ever volunteered to fight and die, that law and order might live.

W. H.

Austin, Texas

1957

Bibliography

The Texas Rangers, Walter Prescott Webb
Gentlemen in the White Hats, C. L. Douglas
Texas, Owen P. White
Scouting Expeditions of the Texas Rangers, Samuel C.
  Reid, Jr.
Indian Depredations in Texas, J. W. Wilbarger
Santa Anna, Callcott (Wilfrid Hardy)
Six Years with the Texas Rangers, James B. Gillett
The Texas Ranger, N. A. Jennings
Rangers and Pioneers of Texas, A. J. Sowell
Bigfoot Wallace, Stanley Vestal

Journal of the Texan Expedition Against Mier, Thomas
    Jefferson Green

Adventures of Bigfoot Wallace, John C. Duval

Early Times in Texas, John C. Duval

The Flavor of Texas, J. Frank Dobie

Index

Alamo, 67
"American Beef Company of Matamoros," 111
Andrews, Captain, 22
Armstrong, J. B., 125, 127-31, 135, 171
Aten, Ira, 165-68, 171
Austin, Moses and Stephen, 8
Austin, in Texas, 14, 30, 52, 71-72, 156

Barnes, Seaborn, 155-56, 159
Bass, Sam, 144-45, 150, 153-60, 164, 171
  born in Indiana, 143
  as cattle rustler, 146
  death of, 161-63
  Murphy's betrayal of, 152, 155-157
  stagecoaches robbed by, 147
  trains held up by, 147-49, 151
Bear Creek, Texas, 138
Bexar County, 69-70
Bexar County Rangers, 37
Big Spring, Nebraska, 147
Black bean legend, 76, 80-82, 84
Black Hills, South Dakota, 146
Blackburn, W. A., 138
Borracho, El, 102
Bowles, Chief, 32, 33
Bowles, John, 34
Brazos River, reservations on, 91-92, 97-98
Brownsville, Texas, 100-02, 112

captured by Cortinas, 103-04
  and Mexican cattle thieves, 116
"Brownsville Tigers," 104

Caldwell, Matt, 55-60, 70-72, 74, 76
Cameron, Ewan, 78
Canadian River, 94, 97
Cattle thieving, 110-11, 117-18
  by Sam Bass, 146
Cherokees, expulsion of, 31-34
  and Mexican plot, 24, 29, 31
Chihuahua, Old, 108
Civil War, 109, 111
Cochran, Dr., 161-62
Coffee, John, 67
Colorado River, 8, 14-17, 34
Colt, Sam, 85
Comanche, Texas, 122-24, 131
Comanches, 24, 34, 38-41, 51-61, 91-98, 164, 171
  and Brazos reservations, 91-92, 97
  expulsion from, 98
  and Hibbons family, 16-17, 20-21
  horse stampede tactic of, 55
  Linnville raided by, 52-53, 57, 98
  massacred at Council House, 43-44
  in peace offer to Rangers, 39-40
  raids renewed by, 92-97
  trapped at Plum Creek, 59-61

Connor, Chris, 156
Cortinas, Juan Nepomuceno, 99,
135
appearance of, 101-02
Brownsville captured by, 103
"Brownsville Tigers" defeated
by, 104-05
as cattle thief, 110-11
cattle thieving ended by Rangers, 117-18
and Ford's Rangers, 106
defeated by, 107-08
Council House Massacre, 43-44,
49, 77
Crockett, Davy, 67

Dallas, 148
Dawson, Captain, 71
Deadwood, South Dakota, 146-47
Denton County, Texas, 148-49,
154-55
Doss, 96
Drunkard, The, 102
Dynamite bomb, and Aten, 165,
167-68

Eastland, William, 78
Espinosa, Guadalupe, 110-11, 117

Fence Cutters' War, 165-68
Fisher, King, 122
Fisher, William S., 40-42, 77-78,
82
Flores, Manuel, 28, 31
Ford, John S. "Rip," 89-90, 92-
97, 109, 135, 171
and Comanches, 93-97
and Cortinas, 106-08
Fort Brown, 103
Fredericksburg, Texas, 138

Frontier Battalion, of Texas
Rangers, 133-35, 140, 152,
165

Gibson, Arch, 56
Gold Eye, 134
Gonzales, Texas, 52
Green, Tom, 111
Grimes, Deputy, 157-58
Guerrero, Mexico, 77

Hacienda Salado, Mexico, 78, 80-
81, 84
Hall, Lee, 170
Hardin, John Wesley, 121-31, 135-
136, 164
Harrell, George, 156, 160, 171
Hays, John Coffee, 66-70, 72, 76-
77, 90, 134, 171
in Mexican War, 84-86, 88
plan for capturing Mexican ar-
tillery, 72-75
vaqueros dealt with, 83-84
Heintzelman, S. P., 104-06, 108
Hibbons, Mrs., 16-17
Horn, Tom, 122
Hornsby, Reuben, 18
Hornsby's station, 14, 17
Houston, Sam, 10, 32, 65, 76-77
Hudspeth, Avery, 45-46, 48
Hughes, John R., 170
Huntsville State Prison, 131, 140
Huston, Felix, 59-61

Indians, on Brazos reservations,
91-92
as enemies of Texas, 4, 12-13
expulsion of, 31-34
from Brazos reservations, 98
High Plains, 4, 57
See also Cherokees; Comanches

Iron Shirt, 92-96, 135
Isbell, Bates, 37-38

Jackson, Andrew, 67
Jackson, Frank, 155-56, 159-61
James, Jesse Woodson, 122
Johnson, Albert Sidney, 38, 40
Jones, John B., 133-34, 165, 171
   and Kimble County clean-up,
     135-36, 138, 140-42
   and Sam Bass, 149-50, 154-58,
     161-62
Jude, Simon, 158-59
Junction, Texas, 138

Karnes, Henry W., 38-41, 67
Kenedy, Ragan, 168-71
Kimble County, Texas, 135-38,
   140-41, 164
Kopperal's Dry Goods store, 158

La Grange, Texas, 71
Lamar, Mirabeau Buonaparte, 32
Linnville Raid, 44-50, 52-53, 57,
   98, 171
Little River, 22
Llano River, 138
Lockhart, Matilda, 43
Lone Wolf, 34-35, 38-39, 41

McCulloch, Ben, 52, 56-60, 62, 67,
   72, 90, 134, 164, 171
   Comanche scout shot by, 54
   Comanche war chief shot by, 60
   in Mexican War, 86
   retreat at Victoria opposed by,
     55
   ride to warn Caldwell, 58
   Victoria warned by, 53
McCulloch, Henry, 67

McNelly, Leander H., 110-14, 116-
   117, 125, 134-35, 165, 171
Majors, Robert S., 98
Massacre, Council House, 43-44,
   49, 77
Matamoros, Mexico, 86, 101, 105
   American Beef Company of,
     111
Mesquite Station, 149
Mexican War, 81, 84-90, 164
Mexicans, and artillery captured
   by Rangers, 72-75, 107
   Brownsville captured by, 103-04
   cattle-stealing by, 110-18
   defeated by Ford's Rangers,
     107-08
   and Mexican War, 81, 84-90
   in plot to retrieve loss of Texas,
     23, 28-29
   San Antonio seized by, 66, 68-
     69, 71
   Texans captured by, 78*ff.*
   viewpoint on Texans, 87-88
Mexico, Guerrero in, captured by
   Texans, 77
   and Mexican War, 81, 84-90
   in revolt against Spain, 8
   Texas as province of, 8
   Texas in revolt against, 9
   vaqueros of, 65, 83, 102, 107,
     116, 118, 171
Mexico City, fall of, 86-88
"Mier Expedition," 77*ff.*
Miller, Alsey, 56, 58
Mississippi River, 146
Monterrey, Mexico, 84, 86
Moore, Deputy, 157-59
Mounted Texas Volunteers, 111
Muk-war-rah, 41-43
Murphy, Jim, 150, 152, 154-57

New York *Herald Tribune,* 170

Oklahoma, 93

Peak, June, 170
Pensacola, Florida, 125-26, 129
Perote Prison, Mexico, 81
Plum Creek, 52, 58-61, 110, 164,
    171
Pockmark Jim, 96

Randall, Barney, 56-57
Rangers, Texas, *see* Texas Rang-
    ers
Red River, 23, 93, 144
Rhodes, Tobin, 45, 48
Rice, Jim, 22-30
Rio Grande, 23, 77, 80, 84-85, 91,
    99, 106, 108, 118, 172
    Brownsville on, 100-05
    Mexican cattle thieves killed at,
        113-14
Rio Grande City, battle of, 107-
    108, 110
Roberts, Dan, 170
Rohrer, Conrad, 20
Rosedale, Miss., 146
Round Rock, Texas, 155-57, 161-
    162, 171
Runnels, Governor, 92

Salado River, 67, 71
    battle of, 73-75, 110
Saltillo, Mexico, 78
San Antonio, 36, 40, 43, 55, 57-
    58, 67, 77
    occupied by Woll, 68-69, 71
    raided by Vasquez, 66
San Gabriel Fork, of Little River,
    22, 25, 27, 29
San Jacinto, battle of, 9
San Marcos River, 58

Santa Anna, Gen., 9, 80
Santa Rita, 104-05
Seguin, Texas, 58
Simms, Innes, 22, 25, 27
Smith, Deaf, 67
Smithwick, Noah, 15-18, 20
Somervell, Gen., 77
Steele, William, 125, 130, 135-36,
    149
"Stranglers," 12
Swain, J. H., 126-27

Tamaulipas, Mexico, 118
Taylor, Zachary, 84-85
Tejanos, as name for Texans, 12
Texas, boom in, outlaws attracted
    by, 132
    Brazos reservations in, 91-92,
        97-98
    Cherokees expelled from, 31-33
    first president of, 10
    as independent nation, 9*ff.*
    Indians ousted from, 33, 98
    legend of black bean in, 76, 80-
        82
    as province of Mexico, 8
    in revolt against Mexico, 9
    and seizure of San Antonio by
        Mexicans, 66, 68-69, 71
Texas Central Rail Road, 148
Texas & Pacific railroad, 148
Texas Rangers, 65*ff.*, 83*ff.*
    and Bass, Sam, 149, 152, 154-
        156, 159, 161, 163
    of Bexar County, 37
    Brazos reservations closed by,
        98
    during Civil War, 109, 111
    Comanches' peace offer to, 39-
        40
    enemies of, 4-5
    and Fence Cutters' War, 165-68

Texas Rangers (*cont.*)
first official corps of, 9-10
Frontier Battalion of, 133-35, 140, 152, 165
and Hardin, 122, 124
Hays's, 83-88
Hibbons boy rescued by, 20
history of, 170-72
in Kimble County "round-up," 137-42
and McCulloch, Ben, *see* McCulloch, Ben
as member of Union, 84
Mexican artillery captured by, 72-75
and Mexican cattle thieves, 111-118
killing of, 113-17
Mexican-Indian plot discovered by, 28-31
in Mexican War, 84-89
in "Mier Expedition," 77*ff.*
oath of, 5, 82
present-day, 174
reason for organization of, 6, 12
reorganization of, to deal with Iron Shirt, 93-97
in 1935, 173
riding ability of, 6-7
skills of, 6
as "special body of irregular troops," 10-12
and State Police, 110
U.S. Army takes over work of, 90-92

in war with Cortinas, 101, 105-108
Texas Regiment, Tom Green's, 111
Trinity River, 8
Tucker, Pettus, 37-38
Tumlinson, John J., 14, 18-19, 54-56, 58

Union Pacific train, held up by Bass, 147, 149
United States Territory of the Indian Nation, 93

Vaqueros, 65, 83, 102, 107, 116, 118, 171
Vasquez, Rafael, 65-66
Victoria, Texas, 53

Walker, Sam, 78, 81, 85-86, 90, 171
Wallace, Bigfoot, 76, 78, 80-82, 85
Walnut Creek, Texas, 20
Ware, Dick, 156, 159, 171
Watts, Major, 48
Webb, Charley, 122-24, 131
Webb, Walter Prescott, 161
Woll, Adrian, 67-69, 71, 73-74, 108
Worth, Gen., 86

Yellow Dog saloon, 123